MW01088405

COMPANION GUIDE

Hey
BEGINNER
WIFE

FINDING ANSWERS IN GOD'S
WORD TO MAKE A MEANINGFUL
DIFFERENCE IN YOUR MARRIAGE

MICHELLE W. LENTZ

BOOKLLO PUBLISHING
MIAMI, FL

Cover design by Beau & Arrow, LLC

Library of Congress Control Number:

ISBN: 979-8-89170-155-7

For Sandy Houston

My mentor and dear friend.
Your example still impacts my marriage and parenting every
day. Thank you for taking me under your wing all those
years ago, xo

Table of Contents

Introduction

Hi Friend!

Congratulations on picking up the *Hey Beginner Wife: Companion Guide*! You've taken an awesome step toward deepening your understanding and applying the spiritual principles from my book **Hey Beginner Wife**. I wrote this guide to help you go even further, turning insightful advice into real, everyday actions.

Inside, you'll find engaging discussions and thought-provoking questions meant to challenge you and help you seek answers in God's Word for the real struggles you face as a wife or future wife. This guide isn't just about gathering information—it's about putting that wisdom into practice and making a meaningful difference in your marriage.

Whether you're exploring this guide on your own, with a small group, or in a Bible study, you're investing in your growth and your relationship. This companion guide builds on the practical advice from my book **Hey Beginner Wife** and shares the spiritual principles that have influenced my own marriage journey.

You're not just reading—you're actively working to enrich your marriage and grow in your role as a wife. I'm thrilled for you and pray that this companion guide supports you in embracing this journey and enriching your marriage. Let's dive in and discover all the great things that lie ahead!

Cheering you on,

Michelle

CHAPTER ONE

Hard-Working

Conversation: Heart to Heart

We just celebrated our wedding anniversary, and guess what everyone said?

"Congratulations!"

Why do we say that on wedding anniversaries? We don't congratulate people on birthdays, but we do congratulate people on college graduations, promotions and anniversaries. Why is that? Because we recognize that these accomplishments take a lot of work, right? These achievements require commitment, dedication, perseverance, and hard work...and marriage does, too.

Marriage *is* hard work. If you don't come to the table with a commitment to love each other on days when your feelings are eclipsed by unpaid bills, disappointments, or the sting of angry words spoken late at night, then you probably won't stay married. A lot of the hard work is taking control of your feelings and addressing the thoughts that rage through your mind when life isn't playing out the way you intended it to.

We were living in our tiny 1,100-square-foot home, and life certainly didn't match my expectations. Some of my girlfriends had the resources to buy their children brand-new clothes. Not me. Some of my girlfriends had a weekly housecleaning service. Not me.

Some of my girlfriends took their families on annual vacations, while we pretended that our two-hour drive to Grandma and Grandpa's constituted a vacation. Often, the hard work of marriage is how we handle the seasons of life that present challenges like this.

Back in the days before our smartphones doubled as cameras, people used video cameras to record their toddler's first steps or summer fun at the splash park. Since we couldn't afford one, I borrowed one from a friend. I thought it was a good alternative to feeling sorry for myself. I planned to record everything I could for a week and then return it to her. Unfortunately, one afternoon while I ran errands with the children, someone broke into our humble home and stole the few electronics we had, including my girlfriend's video camera! Now, not only did we not own a video camera, but we had to find the resources to buy one to replace my girlfriend's camera. We would purchase the video camera I longed for, but it would not be for our family. I cried.

In this instance, the hard work of marriage looked like not resenting my husband for not making more money so we could afford our own video camera, and taking care not to let my thoughts run wild with bitterness. It meant choosing to be thankful for what we had instead of dwelling on what the thief took from us. It meant not wondering what my life would be like if I had married my high school sweetheart. It meant not fantasizing about finding a way out of my situation. The hard work of marriage is often done internally. It's a beautiful thing to recognize and honor those who do this hard work, which is why we offer our congratulations to couples celebrating their anniversaries.

Married couples experience seasons together. No matter how perfect they are for each other, they will experience the very seasons referenced in the traditional wedding vows. "For better, for worse, for richer, for poorer, in sickness and in health, until death do us part." If we anticipate this at the beginning of our marriage, we will have the benefit of perspective when the challenges come our way.

Application: Putting Love Into Action

In Chapter One, *You Can Do Hard Things,* we are reminded that our lives have seasons. As a married couple, you will experience wonderful, happy seasons, and you will also face the difficulty of hard seasons. Some seasons are challenging due to medical issues or a lost job. Knowing that hard times are inevitable, it's helpful to explore what is required of us when we face difficult times and how we can successfully navigate through them.

Does it help you to remember that life happens in "seasons"? Why or why not?

_____

_____

What season is your marriage in right now? Are you in an easier season or a more difficult one? Take a minute to write down a few blessings and/or challenges.

_____

_____

Remembering that seasons change can help provide a healthy perspective in your marriage. Setting goals with your spouse will foster hope and unity.

Inspiration: God's Truth

Have you and your husband agreed on any shared goals for your marriage and family?

_____

_____

I press on toward the goal for the prize of the upward call of God in Christ Jesus. Phil 3:14 NASB

Paul wrote about working to meet a goal in Philippians 3:14. How does he describe what is required of him to meet that goal? What goal is Paul striving toward?

_____

_____

Have you had to press in, or maybe even make a **sacrifice** to meet your mutual goal? This could be a financial sacrifice, a sacrifice of time, hobbies, location, or even friendship.

_____

_____

Have you talked with your husband about how this sacrifice is affecting you, or have you felt it wise to keep it to yourself? If you are keeping it to yourself, have you prayed or journaled about it?

_____

_____

What place does **perseverance or endurance** have in a marriage?

_____

_____

Therefore, since we have so great a cloud of witnesses surrounding us, let us also lay aside every encumbrance and the sin which so easily entangles us, and let us run with endurance the race that is set before us, fixing our eyes on Jesus, the author and perfecter of faith, who for the joy set before him endured the cross, despising the shame, and has sat down at the right hand of the throne of God. Heb 12:1-2 NASB

The writer of Hebrews is mindful that there are men and women who have lived their lives centuries before him, and they too sought to obey and please God. They are now in heaven creating a large group of "witnesses" watching how we are living our lives. Now as they are experiencing the reality of heaven, they watch those of us still on earth in hopes that we, too, will live our lives for the purposes of Christ and run the race we've been given with endurance. This is surely a unique perspective available only to those who live mindful of the fact that their life on earth has purpose.

What does the author say is necessary to lay aside in order to run with endurance?

_____

As we run this race we should fix our eyes on Jesus. Why? Because he is the _____ and _____ of our _____! Why do you think the author gave this advice?

_____

What happens to your thoughts and your attitude when you fix your eyes on something else?

_____

_____

Are you "fixing your eyes" on Jesus? Where is your gaze? Circle any of the below that are distractions for you:

Fear of failure	Comparison	Anxiety
Envy	Anger/Bitterness	Fear of rejection
Financial problems	Exhaustion	Depression/Sorrow
Loneliness	Health issues	Fear of death
Lack of intimacy	Competition	Busyness

Take a minute and lay these distractions at Jesus' feet. He understands and cares.

Jesus is described as the author and perfecter of our faith. Can you describe how that might be encouraging to a young wife to know that Jesus is the author and perfecter of her faith?

_____

_____

What did Jesus focus on that gave him endurance in his goal to be seated at the right hand of God?

_____

_____

Jesus focused on the JOY set before him in knowing you would be his! As we fix our eyes on Jesus, our JOY and the author and perfecter of our faith, we can run our race with endurance. We can know that God is strengthening our faith, even in a tough season!

How are you being called on today to show endurance in your marriage?

_____

_____

_____

Everyone who competes in the games goes into strict training. They do it to get a crown that will not last, but we do it to get a crown that will last forever. Therefore I do not run like someone running aimlessly; I do not fight like a boxer beating the air. No, I strike a blow to my body and make it my slave so that after I have preached to others, I myself will not be disqualified for the prize. I Cor 9:25-27 NIV

Paul compares the Christian life to an athlete training to win a victor's crown. Today he might reference an Olympic gold medal in this analogy. Regardless of what era they are born in, athletes must discipline their bodies and have a serious mindset if they are training to win.

Discipline is prioritizing what you want most over what you want now. Name an area that you have chosen to be disciplined in your marriage:

_____

_____

Now think of a time when you *should* have been disciplined in your marriage but chose not to be. Looking back now, would you choose to do it differently if given the chance? What would you do?

_____

_____

In this scripture, Paul says that part of the reason he disciplines himself is he doesn't want to be disqualified for the prize. How does this mentality apply to a successful and happy marriage?

_____

_____

Training for the Olympics is an all-consuming goal. It is hard work, but the serious athletes know that hard is not the same as bad. In what area of your life do you need to remind yourself that hard is not the same as bad? List three areas that you may have perceived as bad, that are in reality are just hard:

1. _____

2. _____

3. _____

Remind yourself, "I can do hard things!" Hard isn't always bad, it can produce beautiful growth. Knowing this will help you to be disciplined and also persevere in a difficult season.

Then Jesus taught them another parable: "Heaven's kingdom realm can be compared to a farmer who planted good seed in his field. But at night, when everyone was asleep, an enemy came and planted poisonous weeds among the wheat and ran away. When the wheat sprouted and bore grain, the weeds also appeared.

So the farmer's hired hands came to him and said, "Sir, wasn't that good seed that you sowed in the field? Where did all these weeds come from? He answered, "This has to be the work of an enemy!"

They replied, "Do you want us to go and gather up all the weeds?"

"No," he said. "If you pull out the weeds you might uproot the wheat at the same time. You must allow them to both grow together until the time of harvest. At that time, I'll tell my harvesters to make sure they gather weeds first and tie them all in bundles to be burned. Then they will harvest the wheat and put it into my barn."

Matthew 13:24-30 TPT

Perseverance describes a farmer who plants a field and then spends months watching over the field to ensure the health and safety of his crops. Day in and day out, farmers are tasked with watching over their crops and keeping the weeds from overtaking the grain they planted. They may have to irrigate or fertilize their fields in order for their crops to flourish. They may have to protect the crops from insects, rodents, or excessive weeds. Farmers aren't rewarded for their difficult job until it's finally time to harvest their crops and sell them for a profit. If the farmer did not show the *perseverance* of watching over his crops every day he does not get to experience the reward of a bountiful, healthy harvest.

Is there something in your marriage that requires your *perseverance*? Like the farmer, it may be something you're doing that goes unnoticed by almost everyone. But if you choose not to do it, you're also choosing not to experience the reward of a job well done.

Don't miss the blessing of being _____ and choosing _____! It will pay off and your endurance will reap a harvest if you do not give up! It may result in a deeper faith and/or fruitful tangible blessings, but either way, you win!

CHAPTER TWO

Friends

Conversation - Heart to Heart:

Years ago, when Steve lost his job, I didn't know what to do or say. I fumbled along for a few weeks, trying to encourage him. I left him notes by the bathroom sink and a homemade poster on the garage door for him to discover when he got home after we were all fast asleep. I tried to keep the house clean and the kids quiet, but of course, I couldn't do this with toddlers and preschoolers. Even so, I never felt like my encouragement hit the mark. So I finally decided to ask him, "What can I do to support you right now?"

He surprised me with this response, "Nothing really. I'll figure it out. But the fact that you're not complaining and still smiling means more to me than you'll ever know." Sometimes it's the smallest things, even as simple as smiling and having a positive attitude. If you're going through a tough time right now, I'm sorry. Please hang in there. Consider simply asking what you can do to support your spouse. You're walking through the trenches of life, but it won't always be this hard.

My husband is slow, steady, and not easily ruffled. I can be upset and all worked up, and it doesn't fluster him. He listens and sometimes even breaks a smile, as if he enjoys me, even if I'm venting. Having an even-keeled husband helps me return to the center more quickly. Sometimes I need his emotional support and his help processing something. More often than not, I just need him to listen.

Sometimes, we are both in a tough place at the same time. Fortunately, this doesn't happen very often, but when it does, there's usually a moment when we acknowledge that we're both struggling. Rather than demand that Steve focuses on me, or vice versa, we know that we need to be as gentle as we can with each other. Sometimes, we just need some personal space, and at other times, we need to come closer to each other and simply cry and let our emotions out. In difficult times, I've found it best to ask, "How can I show up for you right now? What do you need from me?" I think of these as friendship moments, times that knit the two of us together and strengthen our friendship.

_____

_____

Noah Webster published his original dictionary in 1828 and offered extremely thorough definitions of the word *friend*. Take the time to read each definition as you think about your husband as your dearest friend.

Friend

1. *One who is attached to another by affection; one who entertains for another sentiments of esteem, respect and affection, which lead him to desire his company, and to seek to promote his happiness and prosperity; opposed to foe or enemy.*

    A *friend* loveth at all times. Proverbs 17:17.

2. *One not hostile*; opposed to an enemy in war.

3. *One reconciled* after enmity. Let us be friends again.

4. *An attendant*; a companion.

5. *A favorer;* one who is propitious; as a *friend* to commerce; a *friend* to poetry; a *friend* to charitable institutions.

6. *A favorite*. Hushai was David's *friend*.

7. *A term of salutation*; a familiar compilation.

    FRIEND, how camest thou in hither? Matthew 22:12

    So Christ calls Judas his *friend,* though a traitor. Matthew 26

8. Formerly, a paramour.

9. A *friend* at court, one who has sufficient interest to serve another.

When I consider my husband to be my dearest friend, and when I hope that your husband will be your dearest friend, I am using Webster's first definition. May our husband be the one to whom we are attached by great affection. May we hold for him sentiments of esteem, respect, and affection. May we desire his company more than any other. May we seek to promote his happiness and prosperity. And may he feel all the same toward us!

Inspiration - God's Truth:

Let's look at what the Bible says about friends.

Greater love has no one than this, that someone lay down his life for his friends. You are my friends if you do what I command you. No longer do I call you servants, for the servant does not know what his master is doing; but I have called you friends, for all that I have heard from my Father I have made known to you. John 15:13-15 ESV

According to Jesus, what is the greatest expression of love?

_____

_____

_____

_____

Jesus considers us his friends when we _____what he

_____.

As our friend, Jesus laid down his life for us. He no longer considers us his servants, but his friends. As such, he shares intimate secrets with us and he invites us to share our heart with him. In Proverbs we read about a friendship that is elevated above them all. *"Some friendships don't last for long, but there is one loving friend who is joined to your heart closer than any other."* Prov 18:24 TPT The ESV translation is this, *"There is a friend who sticks closer than a brother."*

Who do you think this scripture is referring to when it references this friend?

_____

_____

_____

Can you imagine a friend that will never leave you? Why or why not?

_____

_____

When I consider that someone would love me so much that they would never leave, my heart rises up to cling to that hope and promise. We first read such a promise in Deuteronomy 31:8 ESV, "It is the LORD who goes before you. He will be with you; he will never leave you or forsake you. Do not fear or be dismayed."

What three things does God promise us in this verse?

1. _____

2. _____

3. _____

What an amazing friend we have in Jesus! A friend who will be with us, never leave or forsake us! Because of these promises, we are encouraged not to be afraid or discouraged. *"A friend loves at all times, and a brother is born for adversity."* In Proverbs 17:17 ESV we have the combination of a friend and a brother's commitment to us. Jesus is both our friend and our older brother, and scripture also teaches us that he is our bridegroom. Jesus sets an example for our husbands of how to love their wives well. And as the bride, we are to respond in kind.

"A dear friend will love you no matter what, and a family sticks together through all kinds of trouble." Prov 17:17 TPT I love this translation of Proverbs 17:17. What kind of love does a dear friend exhibit?

A ____ _____ _____ kind of love!

Can you fathom having a dear friend that loves you no matter what? Do you have a friendship like this with your spouse? Are you a friend to them like this? If so, thank God and express your gratitude below. If not, write a prayer, asking God to help you and your husband become dearest friends.

_____

_____

Given Jesus' example of a friend, how are we to love our husband, our dearest friend?

_____

_____

As family, how are we to respond to one another in times of trouble?

_____

_____

Have you read the story of Ruth in the Old Testament? This young woman was from the Moab kingdom, and her gods and traditions differed from the Hebrews who served the God of Abraham. Yet, a Hebrew man chose to marry her and she left her people and joined him and his mother. Ten years later, Ruth's husband died and her mother-in-law, Naomi, had compassion on her. Naomi encouraged Ruth to return to her land and her people so she could find another husband while she was still young.

But Ruth's heart had turned toward her husband's family and she loved Naomi. Upon hearing that Naomi released her to return to Moab, Ruth replied, *"Do not urge me to leave you or turn back from following you; for where you go, I will go, and where you lodge, I will lodge. Your people shall be my people, and your God, my God. Where you die, I will die, and there I will be buried. Thus may the Lord do to me, and worse, if anything but death parts you and me."* *Ruth 1:16-17 NASB.*

Clearly, Ruth's heart had turned toward her husband and his family. Even after his death, she remained committed to his mother and what was best for her. What words did she use to express her commitment to her mother-in-law?

"Where you _____, I will _____, and where you _____, I will _____. Your _____ will be my _____, and your _____, my _____."

Untold thousands of couples have used this verse in their wedding ceremonies to express to one another that in marriage 'your people will be my people, and your God will be my God.' Perhaps these couples don't realize that Ruth's words were to her mother-in-law and not to her husband? Regardless, her words are extraordinary and express God's heart in marriage that we join ourselves to one another and never leave.

Ruth's story of loyal friendship is remarkable. She goes on to marry one of Naomi's distant relatives and God honored her with a son who went on to be in the lineage of Jesus!

Conversely, there are other wives in the Bible who were not dear friends to their husbands. Consider Job's wife. Job is described as a man who was blameless, upright, fearing God, and turning away from evil. Unbeknownst to Job, God was approached by Satan who accused Job of loving God only because everything was going so well for him. *"(If you) put forth your hand now and touch all that he has; (Job) will surely curse you to your face."* Job 1:11 NASB

God knew Job's heart and that his love for Him was based not on his blessings but on his relationship with God. God granted Satan permission to attack Job, but not permission to harm Job himself. Thus begins a tragic story of loss. Job loses all of his children, his animals, and his health. His closest friends encourage him to curse God. Finally, his wife has had enough and she similarly advises Job, *"Do you still hold fast your integrity? Curse God and die!"* But he said to her, *'You speak as one of the foolish women speaks.'"* Job 2:9-10 NASB

A good friend not only wants the best for us, but also encourages us to honor God. Instead of treating her husband as her dearest friend, Job's wife encouraged him to curse God and die.

What was Job's response to her?

_____

_____

Perhaps you spoke too quickly, or perhaps you were struggling with selfishness, but can you remember a time when your response to your husband encouraged him to take the easy way out?

_____

_____

Another wife in the Bible didn't understand when her husband put God first. King David was so happy that the ark of the covenant (which housed the presence of God) arrived in Jerusalem that David responded with exuberant dancing in the streets. In his gladness, he leapt and danced before "all the house of Israel." We read that his wife looked out of her window and observed her husband leaping and dancing before the Lord.

"When David returned to bless his household, Michal the daughter of Saul came out to meet him. She said in disgust, "How distinguished the king of Israel looked today, shamelessly exposing himself to the servant girls like any vulgar person might do!" 2 Samuel 6:20 NLT

What specific accusation does Michal make against her husband?

_____

_____

David expresses sharp disapproval of her accusations. *"David retorted to Michal, "I was dancing before the LORD, who chose me above your father and all his family! He appointed me as the leader of Israel, the people of the LORD, so I will celebrate before the LORD. Yes, and I am willing to look even more foolish than this, even to be humiliated in my own eyes! But those servant girls you mentioned will indeed think I am distinguished." 2 Sam 6:21-22 NLT*

David's wife Michal did not treat him as her dearest friend. She was more concerned with her reputation before her servant girls than in discovering her husband's cause for rejoicing. Even though David explains to her that his focus was on the Lord and not on his reputation, the Bible does not record that she had a change of heart.

Have you ever shamed your husband without full knowledge of his actions? It's so easy to slip into accusing another. Can you think of a time you have accused your husband prematurely? If yes, list it below and ask God to forgive you and help you to be slower to accuse him.

_____

_____

Application - Putting Love Into Action:

As your husband's dearest friend, what two ways can we be better (**Reference Proverbs 17:17 TPT above**):

1. Love him _____ _____ _____!

2. _____ with him!

Obviously, if we choose to love no matter what and stick with him as our dearest friend, it will become easier to believe the best in every situation. Even if we have been deeply hurt, we can trust the one who will never betray us, Jesus.

Few things can cause the severe pain of a friend's betrayal. Knowing this, and because I love my husband and do not want to cause any pain in his life, I am mindful that if I ever betrayed him, it would be a deep pain. In the book of Psalms, the writer records the pain of an advisor's betrayal. His pain is even more profound because of the trust and camaraderie they once shared.

It wasn't an enemy who taunted me. If it was my enemy, filled with pride and hatred, then I could have endured it. I would have just run away. But it was you, my intimate friend–one like a brother to me. It was you, my advisor, the companion I walked with and worked with! We once had sweet fellowship with each other. We worshiped in unity as one, celebrating together with God's people. Ps 55:12-14 TPT

This verse also brings to mind the marriage relationship and highlights the depth of pain that an intimate friend can inflict because of the unity and confidence once shared. The inference is that intimate friends should always enjoy sweet fellowship with one another devoid of pride and hatred. Both Job and David felt betrayed by their wives. Oh, that we as husband and wife, would be careful not to betray one another.

Practically speaking, it is entirely possible to betray our husbands on a smaller scale than Job and David's wife did. Give a few examples of modern day instances where you know that the wife betrayed her husband in a small but poignant way. (If you are sharing this in a group study, please protect the privacy of the individuals in your example.)

_____

_____

_____

How could the above situation have been handled differently? We all make mistakes in loving our spouse, but with humility and perseverance, we can grow in our "no matter what" love and "stick" with them in life's toughest situations.

_____

_____

_____

Let's turn our hearts back to our husbands and our marriages. Romans 12:10 TPT offers a beautiful encouragement of how to treat one another within the church of God. *"Be devoted to tenderly loving your fellow believers as members of one family. Try to outdo yourselves in respect and honor of one another."* Write this verse as a personal charge to yourself and substitute your husband's name for the references to fellow believers.

Be devoted to tenderly loving _____ as members of one family. Try to outdo yourselves in respect and honor of _____

Let's do the same thing with this verse and make it personal regarding our husband, our dearest friend:

"Love overlooks the mistakes of others, but dwelling on the failures of others devastates friendships." Proverbs 17:9 TPT

Love overlooks the mistakes of _____, but dwelling on the failures of _____ devastates friendships.

By God's grace, may we be devoted to tenderly loving, and overlooking the mistakes or dwelling on the failures of our dearest friend. May we give the grace to our husband that we want given to us. May we believe the best, and trust the Holy Spirit as we grow more intimate with our husband and grow to see him as our dearest friend.

CHAPTER THREE

Extended Family

Conversation - Heart to Heart:

One of our earliest disagreements stemmed from the fact that Steve and I were raised differently. My parents were quite frugal, and his parents weren't. In my home that looked like reusing gently used wrapping paper and repurposing things like empty Cool Whip tubs. So, it bothered me when Steve grabbed four paper towels to use while he was eating his apple. When he only used one but threw them all away, everything within me spiraled and I raced to the trash can to rescue the napkins that weren't used.

As newlyweds, we could afford paper towels. However, after a few years, Steve's small business faced financial difficulties, and we had to tighten our budget. We didn't disclose this to our friends and family; we simply tightened our belts and did things like eliminating paper towels, fast food, frozen pizza, and boxed cereal from our expenses.

Everything was fine until his family visited and couldn't find the paper towels. Steve made the mistake of saying, "Michelle won't buy them for me." He thought he was being light-hearted, simply teasing me as part of the camaraderie he felt with his siblings, who also shared his affinity for paper towels. But then his family prodded a little and asked *me* why I wouldn't buy him paper towels.

I felt completely betrayed and angry. I wasn't going to defend myself and say that we couldn't afford paper towels. I knew they wouldn't understand unless we shared how Steve's business was drying up, and he wasn't ready to share that with them yet. Yes, we could have afforded paper towels if we didn't buy something else... but that wasn't a conversation I wanted to have with his family. So, I walked out of the room, leaving Steve to hang out with his family.

After they left, I told Steve I felt betrayed. He was surprised. He felt he had only been enjoying a shared point of view with his family, and though I understood, it still hurt and bothered me. As we talked, he realized that the laugh with his family had been at my expense, and he apologized. We agreed that in areas of disagreement where we had privately agreed to compromise, in the future we would now own the joint decision in public and present a unified front to others.

We also agreed that when it came to matters that affected our family of origin, we would each communicate the matter to our own family. Going forward, Steve would present our joint decisions to his family, and defend me if necessary. Likewise, if we made a decision not to attend my extended family's gathering, then I would be the one to tell my parents. We felt that this best honored our relationship with our natural born families.

Do you think it's important for your husband to communicate decisions that the two of you have made to his parents, and for you to communicate decisions to your parents?

_____

_____

_____

_____

_____

_____

Inspiration - God's Truth:

Let's look at what God says about relating to parents as grown adults. The Bible gives clear direction in Deuteronomy 5:16 on the relationship between a grown child and his parents. *"Honor your father and your mother as the Lord your God commanded you, that your days may be long and it may go well with you in the land that the Lord your God is giving you."* Adult children are not instructed to *obey their parents,* they are instructed to *honor them.* To honor a parent is to treat them with respect.

Honor your father and mother is one of the Ten Commandments found in Exodus 20. Did you know that? It is the only commandment that comes with a promise. Read Exodus 20:12 and write the promise here.

_____

_____

_____

Have you ever stopped to consider the Ten Commandments and whether or not they apply to you? Look up Exodus 20:1-17 and read the Ten Commandments in Scripture. After reading them, do you think these commandments apply to you today? Why or why not?

_____

_____

_____

God commands us to honor our fathers and mothers, but he also directs us to "leave" them and be joined (or "cleave") to our spouse. *"Therefore a man shall leave his father and mother and be joined (cleave) to his wife, and they shall become one flesh."* Genesis 2:24 NKJV So what does "cleave" mean? For a basic understanding of the word, I love Webster's dictionary definition of "cleave": *"To adhere firmly and closely or loyally and unwaveringly."*

Understanding what God expects of you when you get married will help you transition into the new family you and your husband have created together. Both of you are leaving the parent-child relationship that was once your primary family. You then cleave to one another. The Hebrew word for cleave in Scripture literally means being stuck to someone or something like glue! Isn't that a great visual? A husband and wife are joined together in such a way that no other relationship supersedes theirs. They become one flesh, a single entity.

Reread Genesis 2:24. This verse mentions three things that happen in marriage. Look for the three verbs and write them below.

_____

_____

_____

Application - Putting Love Into Action:

Learning how to prioritize one another as husband and wife while still honoring your parents can be a challenge. It's helpful to remember that honoring means showing them respect and appreciation, not obeying them.

There will be times when you disagree with your parents, but you can certainly disagree respectfully. Let them know that you value their opinion, even if the two of you choose not to take their advice. As in any relationship, you should take turns accommodating the other. At times, his parents/family will accommodate your schedule and choose to have their holiday dinner on a different day. But there should also be times that you change your schedule to go out of your way to accommodate them. Resist the temptation to think that your schedule is more important than theirs. His parents have sacrificed their needs for their son for years. They deserve to be treated with kindness, appreciation, and gratitude.

What does it mean to honor your parents once you're an adult?

_____

_____

Can you give an example of how to honor your parents when they're asking to do something that the two of you have decided not to do?

_____

_____

How would you describe the relationship you have with your mother-in-law?

_____

_____

Can you say that you make the effort to respect her because she is your husband's mother? If so, how do you do that?

_____

_____

Mothers-in-law are people, too. Some are naturally more likable than others. I think you should do your best to pursue a relationship with her. You've made friends before, so you know what it means to foster a friendship. It might take some work and effort, but crafting a relationship with her is possible. Some mothers-in-law are standoffish, selfish, or downright difficult. And it's okay to be honest in your assessment of this woman. If you have vastly different personalities, it's fair to embrace that you'll probably never see things eye-to-eye. Some of you may grieve the fact that you do not have a warm and fuzzy mother-in-law. No matter what you do, she persists with sour responses and impossible expectations; and yes, my friend, this is certainly difficult. *Your* challenge is this: Regardless of her temperament, you're not excused from treating her like Jesus would. Talk to your husband and assure him that you will do your best to be reasonable and kind, but he needs to step in and make sure that you are not mistreated.

One young bride shared with me that she took this exact approach. "I just started to look at my mother-in-law like every other unbeliever I cared about. I prayed for her, and I saw my role as an ambassador of Christ. Perhaps I could win her with kindness, perhaps not. But I tried to treat her the way Jesus would treat her if she walked into his house."

Thinking back on an encounter with your mother-in-law, what would it look like if you focused on treating her how Jesus would treat her the next time you saw her?

_____

_____

"With tender humility and quiet patience, always demonstrate gentleness and generous love toward one another, especially toward those who may try your patience." Ephesians 4:2 TPT

To whom does Paul say that we should especially show gentleness and generous love?

"...especially toward those who may _____

_____ _____*."*

That's a challenging verse, isn't it? There will be some days that we do this well, and other days when we need to cry out to the Lord and ask for his help to love difficult people. Having said that, your mother-in-law might be unreasonable, rude, or cross the line. When this happens, your husband should get involved and stand up to his mother.

Just for fun, let's review a few scenarios.

1. Let's say his parents continually show up to your home unannounced. What happens?

___ You let them in, then call your husband to vent while his parents sit in the living room.

___ You lie and tell them now is not a good time because you're just now leaving for an appointment.

___ You let them in. After the visit, you and your husband decide that he will call them and let them know he has instructed you not to answer the door the next time they come unannounced.

Is there another way you would handle the above scenario?

_____

_____

2. Your husband's parents plan their annual family vacation without asking if you have the dates available, and inform you that they've rented a cabin for the two of you. However, you have already made other plans for that weekend.

Which of the following would most likely be your attitude and response?

_____Discuss it with your spouse and have him call them with your decision.

_____Pick up the phone and immediately call and let them know it was inconsiderate not to ask you first.

_____Thank them and simply rearrange your plans to accommodate them.

Is there another way you would respond? If so, write it here:

_____

_____

3. **Your parents badmouth your spouse's work ethic when they come over and see him sitting on the couch playing a video game. How do you respond?**

_____ You've been frustrated with this very same thing, so you raise your voice loud enough for your husband to hear you and say, "Yeah, he would clearly rather play this game than mow the lawn or contribute to the household!"

_____ Defend your husband and challenge your parents, "That's not a fair statement. He's worked a long week, and he'll be joining us as soon as he finishes this level."

_____ Agree quietly with them. Then confide that he still hasn't fixed the broken shelf in the bathroom and ask your father if he can look at it before he goes home.

Is there another way you would respond? If so, write it here:

_____

_____

Navigating the complexities of family relationships can be difficult. However, as we ask God for wisdom and grow together in our marital relationship, we will succeed! Open communication, willingness to compromise, and unconditional love are absolutely essential. Let's remember that every challenge we face is an opportunity for growth, and with patience, understanding, and a commitment to each other, we can overcome the obstacles that come our way. Let's always strive to honor and cherish our familial relationships, support each other through the tough times, and continue to build a strong foundation and intimacy for our family's future together.

CHAPTER FOUR

Financially Content

Conversation - Heart to Heart:

Steve and I were newlyweds when we were invited to join four other young couples for a party at a friend's house. The hostess planned a game to get the night started. It was basically a "How Well Do You Know Your Spouse" game. The wives wrote down their answers, and the husbands wrote down how they thought their wives would answer, and vice versa.

Years later, I can only remember one question, "If you could buy anything for your home right now, what would you buy?" Since we were all newlyweds, there were still quite a few things we needed for our homes. I answered that I would buy a new couch, and Steve guessed that I would say that so we got a point.

"We went around the room, and the answers varied from a new refrigerator to new curtains for their family room. Then it was Jeannine's turn. "A new shower curtain," she proclaimed, and the room fell silent. The hostess clarified, "No. If you could buy ANYTHING, what would you buy?" Jeannine looked confused, and she said, "A shower curtain."

Her husband smiled and showed his answer. He had written down the words shower curtain, and they got a point, too. He looked at the hostess and said, "I knew you were talking about something bigger, and I know that Jeannine would *really* like a new kitchen table. But I also know how she thinks, and right now, the only thing on her mind is replacing our shower curtain. I figured that's what she'd say, and I was right!"

I love how this husband understood his wife, and I also love how she demonstrated a content heart. In a season where this young couple couldn't afford a new kitchen table, Jeannine looked at her home and set her sights on budgeting for something they could afford.

How would you describe what the word *content* means?

_____

_____

I would describe contentment as a deep sense of peace and gratitude that flows from trusting God's plan for my life. It's about finding joy in the blessings he has given me, whether big or small, and surrendering my desires to his will. Contentment means embracing the present moment with faith, trusting and knowing that God's love and provision are always sufficient, and his timing is perfect. It's a daily journey of seeking his guidance, finding strength in his promises, and rejoicing in his faithfulness, even amidst life's challenges.

Application - Putting Love Into Action:

Take a quick inventory of your own life. Here's a personalized checklist of areas that many women/wives find important for nurturing contentment. Check the areas that you feel you are content in. Place an "x" on any areas that you may need to surrender more to God.

_____ Pursuing passions and personal interests.

_____ Setting and achieving personal goals that align with Biblical values.

_____ Embracing opportunities for self-discovery and growth.

_____ Nurturing close relationships with loved ones and friends.

_____ Practicing self-care that replenishes my energy and spirit.

_____ Honoring emotions and seeking support when needed.

_____ Prioritizing regular exercise that feels good and energizes.

_____ Eating nourishing foods that support overall well-being.

_____ Getting enough restorative sleep to feel refreshed.

_____ Cultivating open communication and deep connection with my spouse.

_____ Sharing moments of laughter, understanding, and mutual support.

_____ Creating meaningful memories together.

_____ Managing finances responsibly and planning for future security.

_____ Feeling confident in financial decisions and contributions.

_____ Celebrating financial milestones and goals achieved.

_____ Decorating my home to reflect my personal style and comfort.

_____ Sharing responsibilities to maintain a tidy and welcoming environment.

_____ Feeling safe and at peace in my home surroundings.

_____ Finding satisfaction and purpose as a wife, a mom, in my career or professional endeavors.

_____ Balancing work commitments with personal life priorities.

_____ Engaging in practices that nourish my spiritual well-being.

_____ Living in alignment with my core beliefs and values.

_____ Finding moments of reflection and gratitude in daily life.

_____ Building and nurturing friendships that bring joy and support.

_____ Participating in social activities that enrich my life and community.

_____ Feeling connected to a network of like-minded individuals.

_____ Taking time for introspection, reflection and personal development.

_____ Embracing opportunities for learning and self-improvement.

_____ Celebrating milestones and achievements along my journey.

Did you find that you are a fairly content person in most areas? Or did the checklist make you feel frustrated? Either way, it's okay! Contentment can be _learned_ as we begin to trust God and experience his grace.

Inspiration - God's Truth:

Did you know that the Bible says that we can learn the secret to contentment? In Philippians 4:12, Paul writes that he has learned the secret of being content in any and every situation. In each translation, circle the words which describe contentment:

I know what it is to be in need, and I know what it is to have plenty. I have learned the secret of being content in any and every situation, whether well fed or hungry, whether living in plenty or in want. (NIV)

I know how to live on almost nothing or with everything. I have learned the secret of living in every situation, whether it is with a full stomach or empty, with plenty or little. (NLT)

I know how to be brought low, and I know how to abound. In any and every circumstance, I have learned the secret of facing plenty and hunger, abundance and need. (ESV)

I know how to get along with humble means, and I also know how to live in prosperity; in any and every circumstance I have learned the secret of being filled and going hungry, both of having abundance and suffering need. (NASB 1995)

Paul's understanding of contentment speaks directly about navigating seasons of plenty or scarcity in finances. Ultimately, money represents our material provision. How do you think Paul learned the secret to being content in all circumstances?

_____

_____

_____

Since contentment is mentioned in the context of having our needs met, let's consider what the Bible tells us about provision.

"So Abraham called the name of that place, "The LORD Will Provide." And to this day it is said, "On the mountain of the LORD it will be provided." Genesis 22:14 NIV

"O LORD our God, all this abundance that we have provided for building you a house for your holy name comes from your hand and is all your own." 1 Chronicles 29:16 ESV

"Your flock found a dwelling in it; in your goodness, O God, you provided for the needy." Psalm 68:10 ESV

As adults, we provide for ourselves by earning money. Most jobs require discipline, responsibility, and a strong work ethic. But ultimately the Bible tells us that God is the one who provides for our needs. We do our part, and then we trust God to watch over us and provide. His provision can look like the wisdom to know where to go to buy your groceries at the best price, a financial gift that allows you to make a down payment on a car, or the blessing of your appliances not breaking down in a season when you have other important bills that need to be paid.

God wants us to remember that *he* is the one who provides for us. We honor him when we look to him for provision. What does Paul tell us in Philippians 4:19? (*"And my God will supply every need of yours according to his riches in glory in Christ Jesus." Philippians 4:19 ESV*)

_____

_____

In our marriages, we can honor God by spending our money carefully. For many of us this will mean living on a budget and being careful not to spend more than we make. It will mean not buying things on credit and incurring interest charges that only add to our financial burden and stress. And it means looking to God as the one who provides for us.

When I am looking to God to provide, I am not going to berate my husband for not making more money. I am not going to complain that my girlfriend can buy things that I cannot buy. I am going to trust that God will meet our needs as we prayerfully ask him to, and then patiently wait on him.

Steve and I used to write down our bills each month, showing the final amounts owed and the dates they were due. Then we'd compare that list with the money we had. When we couldn't pay something we'd circle that item and then prioritize the order in which they would get paid when our next paycheck came in. Oftentimes I took that list and wrote each item in my journal. I titled the lists accordingly, "January Needs" for example. When I prayed, I would thank God in advance for his provision. "Lord, you know that we owe $240 for dental fillings. I'm asking you to show your provision for this. Thank you! I know you'll do it." It buoyed my faith when I wrote them down as a prayer, and then again when I later crossed them off as answered prayers.

So, practically, if you and your husband have been careful with your finances and your car breaks down, what would it look like to be content and trust God in this circumstance?

_____

_____

We discovered that God can be quite creative. Once, when our only car broke down, a family at church heard about it and offered to let us use their family van for a month. We were overwhelmed by their generosity. They simply said, "God put it on our heart, so it's our joy to share with you." Another time, in the face of an unexpected bill, we called to set up a payment plan with one of our creditors to release money to spend on our urgent need for car repairs. They worked with us to lower our monthly payment for six months. By pausing to include God in our financial need, instead of immediately pulling out our credit card, we were able to see him step in and help!

And what if you have an abundance and are able to purchase what you desire for your home without budgeting? According to 1 Timothy 6:17, where are you to put your hope? (*"Command those who are rich in this present world not to be arrogant nor to put their hope in wealth, which is so uncertain, but to put their hope in God, who richly provides us with everything for our enjoyment." 1 Timothy 6:17 NIV*)

_____

_____

Everything comes from him, whether in abundance or in need, and we are to trust God to provide for us. Paul tells us that he learned the secret of being content. I think his secret is twofold. We are *to be grateful for what we have,* and *be expectant that God sees every detail and will provide for us.* When both husband and wife share this attitude, there can be great peace between the two of you.

Write down the two-fold secret of being content (my definition of the secret):

1. _____

2. _____

Being grateful and expectant can shift your attitude into a space of contentment!

When our children were little I got into a car accident, and the damage was my fault. Money was already tight and we couldn't afford to pay our bills, let alone pay for an insurance deductible and car repairs. The weight of knowing that I had just added more strain to our already strained budget was more than I could bear, and I cried all the way home.

I pulled into the driveway and my oldest son ran into the house to get his dad. I'll never forget Steve coming out of the house to the garage. He opened my car door, and gently pulled me into his arms. He held me close and let me cry. "It's okay Michelle, we will figure it out." He spoke so kindly.

He didn't respond as a man carrying a financial burden, he responded as if someone on his team was hurt. He rallied to help. He could have snapped and yelled at me. He could have gotten angry and accused me of being a bad driver, but he was kind. He spoke as a man who trusted that God would provide for us. He trusted that God would continue to make a way to put food on our table, to pay our utilities, and now to pay for car repairs, because that's who he is. God is Jehovah Jireh, the God who provides.

The secret of learning to be content is learning to trust God. When you're married, it doesn't matter how other couples make decisions, spend their money, prioritize their purchases, or plan their families. What matters is how the two of you make YOUR decisions, spend YOUR money, prioritize YOUR purchases, and plan YOUR family. Comparing your situation to another couple will only breed discontentment. Take the time to build your faith and trust in God. Trusting God will be the catalyst to living in contentment, whatever the circumstances. I want to close with a verse that I encourage you to memorize as you learn to be content.

Romans 11:36 (Amplified Bible)

For from him [all things originate!] **God is our provider!** *and through him [all things live and exist]* **(Everything comes from him!)** *and to him are all things [directed].* **(We steward it all to honor him!)** *To him be the glory forever!* **(All the glory is his!)**

Amen.

God is our provider, everything comes from him and can be stewarded for his glory! My prayer for you is that your trust in God grows deeper and deeper. He is a trustworthy God who is always faithful! As you trust him more and more, may your personal contentment and in your marriage flourish.

CHAPTER FIVE

Independent

Conversation - Heart to Heart:

Steve and I married in September, and three months later we had a decision to make: Do we spend Christmas with his family in California or with my family in Illinois? After some discussion, we decided to stay in California and celebrate with his family. It would be the first Christmas without my parents and three brothers. I had the choice to lean in and enjoy the novelty of a new Christmas routine, a varied dinner menu featuring something called *mint pears*, and having a *husband* (!!!) to snuggle with by the lights of a multi-colored Christmas tree, OR I could focus on what was happening without me 2,000 miles away. I could mope around and ruin everyone's experience, including my own; or take the attitude that this marked the first of many adventures with Steve, and rest in the knowledge that there would be plenty of future Christmases to enjoy with my family. My choice to live in the moment with a cheerful heart served both of us well.

When you marry, you leave your father and mother and become united with your husband. Some of you may be young enough that you left your parent's home and support and immediately started living with your husband. Others may have already physically left their parents' home years ago and are now only symbolically transitioning from their home to their husband's home. This is the natural divine order established by God.

49

Either way, a healthy marriage can be yours if you are willing to grow up, embrace adulting, and make the changes necessary in yourself to have the kind of relationship you want. It will require the qualities we've already covered like hard work, contentment, and what we are covering in this chapter, mature independence.

Inspiration - God's Truth:

Paul explains this in his letter to the church at Ephesus. What do you think this verse means? *"Therefore a man shall leave his father and mother and hold fast to his wife, and the two shall become one flesh." Ephesians 5:31 ESV*

_____

_____

_____

Does this verse make you feel uncomfortable, or relieved? Why or why not?

_____

_____

Children live with their parents; then when they are adults, they are ready to leave their parents, marry, and create a new family. It is now time for both of you to give up childish ways. Paul clearly distinguishes between being a child and becoming a man in 1 Corinthians 13:11. Write down the three things Paul did as a child.

"When I was a child, I spoke like a child, I thought like a child, I reasoned like a child. When I became a man, I gave up childish ways." 1 Cor 13:11 ESV

Paul _____, _____, and _____ like a child.

What one thing did Paul do when he became a man?

_____

_____

_____

Application - Putting Love Into Action:

Reread the story of Lauren and Tyler in Chapter 7. Lauren wants Tyler to celebrate her birthday with her. What event is happening at the same time that conflicts with her birthday?

_____

_____

_____

How does Lauren respond when Tyler tells her that his sister's rehearsal dinner and wedding will be on her birthday??

_____

_____

Lauren says Tyler told his sister that they could not be at her rehearsal dinner because they have a tradition of celebrating his wife's birthday at a specific restaurant. What attribute best describes her attitude? Circle your answer.

Flexible	Compromising	Manipulative
Coercive	Understanding	Controlling

Of the above attitudes, which one do you think a mature wife should employ when asking her husband to attend an event?

_____

_____

_____

Lauren tries to get her way by pouting and coercing. Lauren is dogmatic about attending an event because it conflicts with her birthday. Because of this, she is unable to take into account that Tyler's sister's wedding is a significant life event and means alot to him. Instead, she's only focusing on the fact that she wants to be celebrated on her birthday weekend.

A mature woman does not demand or pout when she doesn't get her way. Pouting, sulking, and complaining are all ways women try to manipulate or coerce their boyfriends and husbands.

The fact that Lauren is pressuring Tyler to prioritize her birthday instead of considering the one-time life event of his sister is manipulative. Perhaps she thinks she is setting a good boundary within her new marriage and convincing Tyler it is for the sake of setting a precedent and protecting their marriage?? Perhaps she is actually only thinking about herself?? Do you think it is selfish of Lauren to demand that her birthday be celebrated instead of attending Tyler's sister's rehearsal dinner?

Have you experienced a similar attitude in a conflicting event with your partner? Why did you feel that way?

Lauren might need to grow in learning how to compromise. To do this, Lauren must learn to consider the bigger picture, and prioritize her husband. This will happen when she challenges herself to realize that her birthday happens every year and a wedding is a one-time life event. Laying down her desires to show consideration for her husband may take humility and selflessness, and require her to consider her husband's desire as more important.

Inspiration - God's Truth:

What does Philippians 2:3 say? (Write it below)

Phillippians 2:3 would be a great verse for Lauren to reference in this situation: "Do nothing from selfish ambition or conceit, but in humility count others more significant than yourselves."

Does this verse bring conviction from the Holy Spirit to you? Yes or No? _____

It makes me want to make sure I am humbly considering my husband's needs before my own. Does Phillippians 2:3 make you want to say, "But what about me!?" If so, I'm sure you are not alone. Do you trust that God will take care of your desires?

Take a minute and read this Scripture over yourself, writing your name in the blank to personalize it.

Psalm 37:4

[When I] Delight myself in the Lord, he will give me [your name   ] the desires of my [your name   ] heart.

Remembering that you can trust God to take care of you, makes it easier to compromise in a disappointing situation.

Application - Putting Love Into Action:

Lauren also had difficulty putting her desires aside and encouraging Tyler to enjoy the celebration of his sister. A mature woman can master her desires and delay gratification. Learning to delay gratification is something your parents should have taught you, but if they didn't then it's time for you to learn it now. Yes, it is disappointing not to get what you want right away, but a mature woman knows how to live in the moment, deal with the disappointment, and consider the needs of those around her.

You might be uncomfortable as you become more mature and learn how to consider others as more important than yourself. Regardless of the discomfort, let me encourage you to look ahead to the goal of becoming a mature, capable, and independent woman. You will have so much respect for yourself once you've learned this. Imagine looking at yourself and admiring who you've become, and let that goal inspire you to do the uncomfortable work necessary to grow and mature.

Here's another excerpt from Chapter 5. "An independent married woman demonstrates selflessness and assertiveness. She knows when to prioritize her needs while also understanding the importance of compromise and sacrifice when it benefits the relationship. Confidence and competence characterize her demeanor, allowing her to both lead and follow as the situation demands."

A mature woman knows how to balance conflicting emotions, and when to choose one over the other. Referring to the above paragraph, write the corresponding actions on the lines below.

An independent woman can demonstrate both selflessness and_

_____.

A mature woman can prioritize her needs, while also understanding the importance of _____ and

_____.

A confident woman can both lead and _____

_____.

Take a minute to thank God for the privilege of being a woman who can be both independent and interdependent. Ask him to bring you to a place of beautiful balance as a wife.

CHAPTER SIX

Generosity

Conversation - Heart to Heart:

My girlfriend tells the story of the day her father gave away all of their living room furniture. She was in elementary school when he brought the family together and told them of a fire that had destroyed his coworker's home, "Everything they have is gone. Everything. I've decided that we're going to give them our living room furniture to help them out." Young Sandy watched as the rental van pulled up and the men loaded their furniture into the back hatch. Over time, they replaced their living room furniture, but can you imagine walking by an empty room every day and knowing that your father's sacrificial giving blessed another family in their crisis? Growing up in a home with such a generous father greatly influenced her, and when I met Sandy I immediately noticed how freely she gave. Later, when she shared this story with me, it all made sense.

Sandy and her father were both marked by generosity, and their example followed me into my marriage. Years later, when I learned that a family in our community had lost their home, I recalled Sandy's father and asked Steve if we could donate something to make a difference. We had a sofa and television in the back room that we volunteered. I gathered extra blankets, pots and pans, some dishes, and our sleeping bags. It certainly wasn't a room full of furniture, but what a joy to give it away!

Have you ever been the recipient of an extravagant act of generosity? How did it make you feel?

_____

_____

_____

Which is harder for you? Circle your answer:

Giving - Being the giver

Receiving - Being the receiver

Why is it hard for you? Sometimes it is just as hard to receive as it is to give. What do you think is hindering your giving or receiving?

_____

_____

Generosity is integral to a happy marriage. It prompts us to praise our spouse instead of critiquing them, to serve them when we are tired, and sometimes a generous heart inspires us to give up something we hoped to buy and instead encourage our spouse to finally spend the money on themselves this month.

And when there is generosity in a marriage, it spills over into the lives of our children. One time in particular stands out to me as an example of this. My daughter had a darling little designer purse that she purchased with her own money. If you can picture the kind of purse that makes your whole outfit sing, then you can imagine how put together she felt when she grabbed this particular purse on her way out the door that morning. Later that day, as she unloaded her groceries on the moving belt, the cashier noticed her adorable purse and gushed, "Oh my gosh, I LOVE your purse. It is SO cute!!!" When my daughter saw the delight in the cashier's eyes, she knew that she wanted her to have it. So she grabbed a grocery bag, dumped out the contents of her purse, and handed the stunned woman her purse. "I want you to have it!" she exclaimed. "It would just make me so happy to know that you get to enjoy this purse next!"

Have you ever been moved to give something away that didn't make sense to anyone else?

_____

_____

What emotion do you think you would feel if you unexpectedly gave someone a gift they weren't expecting?

_____

_____

Inspiration - God's Truth:

We serve a generous God. He is characterized by giving and giving generously. You're probably familiar with this verse, but when you read it this time, notice the verb. I've left it blank for you to fill in.

"For God so loved the world that he _____ his only begotten Son, that whoever believes in him should not perish but have everlasting eternal life." John 3:16 ESV

God gave the ultimate gift when he gave us Jesus! He is the giver of all good things! His heart is generous and longs to give to us and through us. He wants us to experience the true joy of giving and receiving. Yes, he's *that* good!

2 Corinthians 9 goes so far as to say that God loves hilarious giving!

"Let giving flow from your heart, not from a sense of religious duty. Let it spring up freely from <u>the joy of giving</u>–all because <u>God loves hilarious generosity!</u> Yes, God is more than ready to overwhelm you with every form of grace, so that you will have more than enough of everything–every moment and in every way. <u>He will make you overflow with abundance</u> in every good thing you do." 2 Cor 9:7-8 TPT

I underlined three phrases in this verse. Write each phrase in the lines below:

_____

_____

_____

_____

If you would like to experience the joy of giving, hilarious generosity, or overflowing with abundance, imagine that you're sitting across the table from Jesus and write down your request as though you were talking to him.

_____

_____

_____

_____

Generosity takes on many forms. Whether we share our home, time, resources, or finances, it's all generosity and it's all about thinking of others. When Jesus was asked which commandment ranked above them all, he replied that there were two. *"Love the Lord your God with all your heart and with all your soul and with all your mind and with all your strength. The second is this: Love your neighbor as yourself." (Mark 12:30-31 NIV)* As a married couple, keeping these two commandments in mind would be a great foundation for your marriage.

Over and over again, Jesus spoke about the importance of how we treat others. C.S. Lewis gives us an indication of why our relationship with other people is so important to the Lord. "There are no ordinary people. You have never talked to a mere mortal. Nations, cultures, arts, civilizations -- these are mortal, and their life is to ours as the life of a gnat. But it is immortals whom we joke with, work with, marry, snub and exploit."[1] Every single person in our lives was created by God and matters to him. When we snub our neighbor, God takes it personally. This explains why hospitality is highlighted in the Bible several times.

"When God's people are in need, be ready to help them. Always be eager to practice hospitality." Romans 12:13 NLT

_____

[1]   C.S. Lewis, *The Weight of Glory,* (Harper One: New York, 2001) 46.

"Don't forget to show hospitality to strangers, for some who have done this have entertained angels without realizing it!" Hebrews 13:2 NLT

"I tell you the truth, when you did it to one of the least of these my brothers and sisters, you were doing it to me!" Matthew 25:40 NLT

"Cheerfully share your home with those who need a meal or a place to stay." 1 Peter 4:9 NLT

Choose one of the four verses above and write how you can practically apply it to your life.

Application - Putting Love Into Action:

Can you think of anyone in your life that exemplifies hospitality? What do you feel like when you're with them?

_____

_____

_____

How do you think your husband would respond to the idea of practicing hospitality and having people over to your home?

_____

_____

_____

Is there anything about your home that you think prevents you from practicing hospitality?

_____

_____

_____

In what ways are you generous? How about your husband; in what ways is he generous?

_____

_____

_____

Most people aren't looking to be entertained. They simply want to sit and enjoy some time with YOU. Imagine that you wanted to come to my home. I'm going to bet that you don't want to come over so you can see what my home looks like. You want to come over to sit and visit with me, right?

In today's day and age, it is an extravagant treat to sit down and share time with someone who stops what they're doing to spend time with us. Hospitality is more about creating an environment where people *feel* welcomed and seen. Remember, it's not about what your home looks like, it's how you make your guests feel when they are in your home! Take that to heart when you are trying to get everything in your home just-right before inviting someone over. Start where you are, with what you have, and focus on creating an environment where your guests will feel loved and honored. Remember that true hospitality is when people leave feeling better about themselves and not better about you. Hospitality is simply an opportunity to show love and care. What a wonderful opportunity we have to represent Jesus and generously love others through hospitality!

CHAPTER SEVEN

Respect

Conversation: Heart to Heart

Imagine that you are Lexie and you are married to Ryan. You are in a conversation with a group of new friends who are complaining about their husbands. The attention turns to you, "Lexie, do you respect your husband?" You answer something along the lines of, "Oh gosh, I have a great husband. He just told me that he's surprising me with a trip out of town this weekend. But do I respect him? Not really. Honestly, we're working on some things. He can't seem to pick up his laundry, never pitches in with cleaning, conveniently forgets his dry cleaning, and can't even handle his own doctor's appointments. No, it's seriously like having another child around. Nothing dramatic to respect. *But that doesn't mean I don't love him!*"

Application: Putting Love Into Action

I first heard this scenario used in a presentation illustrating the differences between men and women. The speaker told us that Ryan (and the majority of men) would be absolutely *devastated* to hear their wife speak like this. Really? I was surprised. It didn't seem like that big of a deal to me.

What was your response when you read this? Does it make sense to you that Ryan would be devastated to hear that Lexie didn't respect him?

_____

_____

So what is the flip side of a conversation like that, of men talking to men? Let's imagine your husband Ryan is grabbing a drink with a few other guys. One of them blurts out, "Ryan, do you still love your wife?" He pauses, and responds, "Lexie is amazing. I couldn't ask for a hotter wife. She manages our kid's schedules like a boss. But, um, it's not what I thought it would be. I like her, don't get me wrong, but no, I honestly can't say that I'm still in love with her."

How would you respond if you overheard your husband say something like this about you?

_____

_____

In a relationship, BOTH men and women need respect *and* love. Interestingly enough, both men and women might define them differently. How would you define ***respect*** in a marriage relationship?

_____

_____

How would you describe *love* in a marriage relationship?

_____

_____

Prior to understanding what respect means to men, I used to think that it was something that had to be earned. I would confer respect to individuals based on their actions or their position. Therefore, when I was newly married, I would have said that I didn't "respect" my husband. I considered him my equal and planned to treat him accordingly. Do you see respect as something that needs to be earned, or as a choice that you make?

_____

_____

When I was first challenged with the idea that I communicated disrespect to my husband when I corrected him, it surprised me. This prompted me to start observing how men corrected each other. I wanted to see how they responded when they disagreed and how they handled it when someone underperformed. I started paying attention to how Steve interacted with other baseball coaches and our neighbors. I only observed one occasion where a man lost his temper and said something disrespectful to Steve. When I asked Steve about this incident and why he didn't respond in kind, he explained that he knew this man's home life was stressful, so he decided to give him a pass. In the midst of conflict, Steve considered the whole picture and determined that a respectful response was still in order.

Can you think of an interaction between two men that surprised you because you expected them to get angry with each other, but instead they gave each other the benefit of the doubt?

_____

_____

Thinking of that same situation, imagine that it was two women. How would the conversation be different?

_____

_____

The following statements are from **_Hey Beginner Wife_** with blanks left for you to fill in your husband's name. After reading each one, consider your heart-response. Can you respond to your husband in these ways? If any of these statements are particularly challenging to you, take some time to consider why you feel resistance. In the lines below each statement, write how you'll respond to each definition of respect in your own marriage.

_Respect is treating _____ as a capable, grown man; honoring the fact that although he may do it differently than me, he will still get the job done. It means honoring his capabilities without criticism._

_____

_____

Respecting _____ does not mean conceding that he is more intelligent than I am.

_____

_____

Respecting_____ is choosing to approach him as someone who is also intelligent.

_____

_____

Respecting _____ doesn't mean that I cannot offer my ideas, it means not shutting down his ideas and acting as if my ideas are better.

_____

_____

Respecting _____doesn't mean that I cannot disagree with him. It is acknowledging that his opinion has value and disagreeing respectfully.

_____

_____

Respect is showing appreciation for all that _____ does and not taking him for granted.

_____

_____

Respect is not second guessing his decisions, and not playing devil's advocate every time _____ makes a decision.

_____

_____

Respect is trusting _____ to get the job done without my reminders, and without demanding that he do it my way.

_____

_____

Respect is believing that if _____ is presented with a problem, he is able to figure out the solution and take care of it without my oversight.

_____

_____

Respect is extended even in the face of weakness and poor behavior. I can respect _____ and still disagree with his behavior.

_____

_____

Respecting_____ is always giving him the benefit of the doubt.

_____

_____

Conversation: Heart to Heart

In the early years of our marriage, Steve pushed back when I challenged his decision to watch television one Sunday afternoon. Instead of coming right out and telling him that I thought he was being lazy, I pointed out that he still had an unfinished work project to complete before the next morning. At the time, I didn't realize that I projected a lot of my approach to how I scheduled my own time on to him and how he spent his time. And of course, I thought my way was best.

Steve responded by telling me that he wanted to watch television, that I should not worry about his project, and that my "tone" was grating. At the time I responded, "My tone? I haven't raised my voice or changed anything about the way I'm talking to you. What do you mean by *my tone*?" Unfortunately, Steve didn't know how to explain what he meant. He'd never been married before and never had another woman (besides his mother) question how he chose to spend his time. He didn't like it. But like most men, he didn't have much experience with articulating how someone else's actions made him *feel*.

If he had simply said, "You sound like my mother. Please don't correct me for watching TV, and please trust me to organize my own time," it would have made sense. What I've come to realize now is that most men think we know that we shouldn't correct them, but we are doing it anyway because a.) we don't trust them, b.) we believe they are incapable, or c.) we think our way is better than their way.

Application: Putting Love Into Action

Take a deeper look at the last sentence in the paragraph above.

"What I've come to realize now is that most men think we know that we shouldn't correct them, but we are doing it anyway because a.) we don't trust them, b.) we believe they are incapable, or c.) we think our way is better than their way."

Ask yourself the hard questions:

a. Do I trust my husband?

b. Do I believe my husband is capable?

c. Do I regularly give him the freedom to do things his way? If you answered no to any of the above. Take a minute and ask God to help you do better.

Have you had any interactions with your husband that remind you of the one I had with Steve when I told him I thought he should work on his project, and not watch television?

Think about the comments you make to your husband. Do they sound like a mother talking to her son? Do you correct, instruct, or bring up examples from the past? Going forward, how can you adjust your responses so you sound like a woman who believes in her husband and his abilities?

Now that your eyes are open to the fact that men want to be treated as capable adults, I've got something for you to try. Think of one or two things that you appreciate about your husband or that he does really well. You're going to use these to formulate a "respect compliment." Write them here:

_____

_____

_____

Now, take the thing you appreciate about your husband and insert it into the following sentence:

"Honey, I've been thinking about how much I respect you lately. You do such a great job of _____

_____, and I wanted you to know that I really appreciate you."

Next, you'll want to practice saying that sentence so that when the time comes you can effortlessly say it out loud to your husband. If you aren't in the habit of complimenting him, this might take some effort. You'll have to practice saying it loud enough so it doesn't come out like a whisper. You want him to hear you when you say, "I've been thinking about how much I respect you." It's okay to nonchalantly say this to him, and then walk out of the room.

He might be so surprised that he'll wonder if he heard you correctly. He might even come looking for you to ask you what you said because hearing this compliment from you is going to be music to his ears. You're telling him a specific reason that you appreciate him, and you're telling him that you admire him. (Respect/admire/honor are all very similar.) He needs to hear this from you. Instead of withholding your admiration because he hasn't earned it, you can choose to give him the gift of honoring him for what he *actually does for you.*

As we've talked about respect, what is your biggest takeaway?

_____

_____

_____

What do you think you'll begin to incorporate in your own marriage?

_____

_____

_____

Inspiration: God's Truth

I'd like to share a Scripture that illustrates the intersection of love and respect. When we choose to give our husbands the benefit of the doubt, this verse highlights how believing the best in others is an act of love as well.

1 Corinthians 13:7a (TPT) says, *"Love is a safe place of shelter, for it never stops believing the best for others."*

Here are a few more scriptures to meditate on regarding respect, beginning with several different translations of Ephesians 5:33, one of the most often quoted Scriptures on marriage:

Eph 5:33 NASB *"However, let each one of you love his wife as himself, and let the wife see that she respects her husband."*

Eph 5:33 TPT *"So every married man should be gracious to his wife just as he is gracious to himself. And every wife should be tenderly devoted to her husband."*

Eph 5:33 NIV *"However, each one of you must also love his wife as he loves himself, and the wife must respect her husband."*

Eph 5:33 NLT *"So again I say, each man must love his wife as he loves himself, and the wife must respect her husband."*

1 Pet 2:17 NLT *"Respect everyone, and love the family of believers. Fear God, and respect the king."*

Prov 21:19 TPT *"It's better to live in a hut in the wilderness than with a crabby, scolding spouse!*

Prov 21:19 NLT *"It's better to live alone in the desert than with a quarrelsome, complaining wife."* (Other versions say crabby, scolding, cross, petulant, fretful, contentious, vexing.)

Matt 7:1-4 MSG *"Don't pick on people, jump on their failures, criticize their faults – unless, of course, you want the same treatment. That critical spirit has a way of boomeranging. It's easy to see a smudge on your neighbor's face and be oblivious to the ugly sneer on your own. Do you have the nerve to say, 'Let me wash your face for you,' when your own face is distorted with contempt?"*

Matt 7:1-4 NIV *"Do not judge, or you too will be judged. For in the same way you judge others, you will be judged, and with the measure you use, it will be measured to you. Why do you look at the speck of sawdust in your brother's eye and pay no attention to the plank in your own eye? How can you say to your brother, "Let me take the speck out of your eye,' when all the time there is a plank in your own eye?"*

Rom 12:10b NIV *"Honor one another above yourselves."*

CHAPTER EIGHT

Sex

Conversation: Heart to Heart

"Yes! I would absolutely love a *lingerie* shower!" My bridesmaids had asked me if I had any requests for the bridal shower they were hosting on my behalf. I figured that I had a lifetime to acquire fluffy rugs and Pottery Barn bowls, but I only had one honeymoon, and I could hardly wait to enjoy a sexy 10-day vacation with my soon-to-be *husband*. I looked forward to an entire wardrobe of lingerie and many opportunities to enjoy all the tiny, lacy creations.

I provided my measurements, sizes, and favorite colors, and the girls included them with the shower invitations. After a beautiful lunch of chicken salad and watermelon, we opened the pink and ivory-wrapped gifts in the living room. I opened lovely bra and panty sets, teddies, and nighties, and then I picked up a gift from Steve's grandmother, who couldn't be there with us. Hers was a larger, heavier box. Perhaps it was a robe? I tore off the wrapping paper, only to discover a full-length, long-sleeved flannel nightgown fit for a grandmother sleeping in a snowy log cabin.

What was I supposed to do with a granny gown? My heavens, I was getting **married**!! I couldn't imagine ever wanting to be wrapped up in flannel again. My life as a sexy wife was finally upon me! After we were married, I told Steve what his grandmother had given me and he immediately said, "I hope you threw it away!"

When it comes to our sexuality, some of us are comfortable talking about details and some of us aren't. I'm fairly sure Steve's grandmother was not, at least with me anyway. Our experience with sex and sexuality is unique to everyone. It is challenging to talk openly about something God intended to be private. Each one of us has a different story. Some of us grew up hearing that sex was a natural part of life and were encouraged to begin exploring our sexuality at an early age. Others lived in homes where sex was never mentioned, and they never saw open displays of affection between their parents. Many stories include abuse or exposure to pornography at a young age. We've grown up in a broken world, but God is big enough to take our stories and restore us to sexual health.

God created sex, and everything he created is good. Before we move on, I invite you to pray and ask God to come alongside and encourage you, and for some of you...comfort you, in this vulnerable place.

> *Lord, sex stirs up more emotions than I anticipated. It makes me feel vulnerable, frustrated, scared, and angry. Sometimes I feel like crying or retreating; I feel alone, exposed, undesired, not good enough, lacking, and sad.*

> *I struggle to fully believe that sex is good, but I want to. I long to believe that I am not disqualified from experiencing its beauty. Help me trust that you are for me and not against me.*

*Please meet me in this place of uncertainty and fear. Comfort me, Lord. Give me hope for my future. Help me feel beautiful on the inside, knowing that **your** love defines my worth. Draw close to me; help me to know that you care about details like this. Lord, I ask you to hold the pain of my past. Help me to hear, believe, and understand what is true—that you love me deeply. Help me grasp the depth of your love and find peace in your presence.*

Psalm 139:1-2 TPT records King David's understanding of how intimately aware God is of him. *"Lord, you know everything there is to know about me. You perceive every movement of my heart and soul, and you understand my every thought before it even enters my mind."*

David finds comfort in knowing that God understands him so well. He is in awe that God knows him better than he knows himself. Read Psalm 139 slowly. How does it make you feel to know that the God of the universe intimately knows everything about you and has planned a wonderful future for you?

_____

_____

Psalm 139:5 TPT records an amazing picture of what God does for us: *"You've gone into my future to prepare the way, and in kindness you follow behind me to spare me from the harm of my past."* Have you ever been aware that God has gone before you to prepare the way? Have you had a "God-encounter" (you may not

have even known it was him at the time!) that made you know he
was intimately involved in your life? What ways has he revealed his
intricate involvement in your life to you?

_____

_____

Consider the picture of God following behind you in kindness to
spare you from the harm of your past. How amazing and how kind
is our God that he cares about how our past affects our future! Paul
wrote about this in Rom 8:28. Write that verse below:

_____

_____

Pray this with me: *Lord, please go into my future to prepare
a way for me and my husband. Please make all things of my
past somehow work together for my good. Thank you for
your amazing kindness toward me as you follow behind me
to spare me from the harm of my past!*

Sit and ponder this for a moment. What does it mean to you that
God follows behind you to spare you from the harm of your past?
What picture does this evoke in your mind? What emotions are
stirred up as you ponder God working to spare you from past pain?

_____

_____

God knows everything about you, your whole story, and he ADORES you! He is on your team, he's on your side. If he was picking teams for dodgeball, he'd pick you first. You're his favorite, my friend. And because he is crazy in love with you, he went over and above and wants to bless you with the gift of an enjoyable and satisfying sex life with your husband!

> *Lord, please help me believe that you want me to enjoy, and be deeply satisfied with, my sex life.*

Let's talk about this for a minute! God made sex to feel amazing. Orgasms feel incredible. He didn't have to do that. He could have made us with a natural instinct to have sex just for reproduction. The sex act could have been as simple and mundane as sneezing or coughing, but God went above and beyond when he designed our bodies. Did you know that the clitoris exists solely for pleasure? That's it. Isn't that remarkable? God added that to bless you!

At the age of 37, an MRI revealed a large tumor growing in the meninges of my brain, which was crushing my olfactory nerve. Successful surgery removed the tumor but left me without the ability to smell. I used to enjoy the scent of freshly brewed coffee, newly mowed grass, and my husband's aftershave, but after the surgery, I lost my sense of smell. Without an olfactory nerve, it's impossible to smell. I went through a period of grieving for the loss of my sense of smell, but then something unexpected happened. I developed a greater appreciation and awe for the world that God created. I realized that our sense of smell is, for the most part, an incredibly generous gift that enhances our experience on Earth. Yes, the ability to smell mildew alerts us to the presence of mold and signals the need to remove it for health reasons. Smelling gas in the kitchen could indicate a gas leak that requires immediate attention. I realized, however, that 95% of the things we smell are for our pure enjoyment and to enhance our lives! God chose to add unique fragrances to each flower, and food tastes better because of its aroma. The countryside comes alive with new scents after a fresh rain. Smelling is a bonus that blesses us, and the different sensory experiences of the erogenous zones of our body are yet another of God's many creative and abundant blessings for us.

Have you ever considered that God had a creative choice when he designed our bodies for reproduction? He had a choice, and he chose to design us for pleasure and intimacy. How does that make you feel?

_____

_____

Do you feel like you are enjoying sex with your husband the way God intended for you to enjoy it?

_____ Yes

_____ No

_____ I Don't Know

If your answer was "No" or "I Don't Know" then be honest and ask the God who created you to help you with the simple prayer below. He will do it!

> *Lord, I don't feel like I'm fully enjoying sex in the way you intended for me to enjoy it. Please help me to discover and truly enjoy sex in the way you created it and intended it to be.*

Inspiration: God's Truth

Let's explore what the Bible says about sex to give us a framework to build upon.

"For everything God created is good, and nothing is to be rejected if it is received with thanksgiving." 1 Tim 4:4 NIV

Everything God created is _____!

Nothing is to be rejected if it is received with _____

_____.

"For *everything* comes from him and exists by his _____ and is intended for his _____. All glory to him forever! Amen." Rom 11:36 NLT

Everything that God created is good and intended for his glory. That truth is going to land in different places with different people. You may even find it hard to believe. But if we lean into this truth and ask God to help us believe it, I think this is a prayer he will take great pleasure in answering.

In your own words, write a prayer asking God to help you believe that *everything* he created is good.

_____

_____

_____

_____

What are some things that you have a hard time believing he created for good? Is it hard for you to believe sex was created for your good? Write down anything you struggle with and then write beside it a way you could see it as good.

Something I struggle with believing is good:	How it can be/or is created for good:

Now take a moment to consider what parts of your sex life you can be thankful for today. What parts of your sex life do you hope to be thankful for in the future? (Bolster your faith and thank God in advance!) Write a prayer of thanksgiving either for something God has given you or something you believe he will do for you, or simply thank him for who he is.

_____

_____

_____

Have you ever read the Song of Solomon in the Old Testament? It's astonishing—God dedicated an entire book of the Bible to explore the passionate desires of lovers. Bible scholars interpret it as an allegory of Christ's deep love for his bride, the church. Understanding the natural longing between a husband and wife, God poetically portrays a couple utterly captivated by each other. The book unfolds through the voices of King Solomon, his bride-to-be, and their surrounding community. After Solomon comes into the garden to join her, the community around him proclaims, "Eat, friends, drink, and be drunk with love!" Song 5:1b ESV Imagine God proclaiming this to you and your husband! "Hey you two, be drunk with love!! Get so passionate about one another that your hunger is satiated and your thirst is quenched."[2]

For our purposes, I'd like to highlight the sensuality of this woman. She is *expressive* toward him. Consider a few of the things she articulates about him.

"How handsome you are, my beloved." Song 1:16 NASB

"Like an apple tree among the trees of the forest, so is my beloved among the young men." Song 2:3 NASB

"My beloved is mine and I am his." Song 2:16 NASB

_____

2   This section about the Song of Solomon is heavily influenced by the book *Intimate Issues* by Linda Dillow and Lorraine Pintus. (Colorado Springs: Waterbrook Press, 1999.)

Calling your husband an apple tree among the trees of the forest doesn't sound like a compliment our husbands would value today. How would you rewrite the sentiment of her compliment in such a way that your husband would know that you value him above all others?

_____

_____

_____

Solomon's fiance is **uninhibited**. She is comfortable asking her man where to put his hands. Write Song 2:6 in the lines below and underline where she asks him to place his hands.

_____

_____

_____

Song 4:15-16 TPT records this exchange:

The Bridegroom-King: "I have come to you my darling bride, for you are my paradise garden!"

The Shulamite Bride responds: "Come walk with me until I am fully yours. Come taste the fruits of your life in me."

She is **responsive** to her man and says, "Come taste the fruits of your life in me." Thinking of you and your husband, take a moment to remember a time that your husband complimented you and perhaps you didn't respond favorably. If you were uninhibited, how might you respond to him differently? Write a compliment that you could give to your husband.

_____

_____

_____

NASB translates Song 4:16 in this way: *"Make my garden breathe out fragrance, Let its spices be wafted abroad. May my beloved come into his garden and eat its choice fruits!"* Imagine that she is whispering these words to her husband, and inviting him to love her. Can you see God's intention for intimacy in this verse?

The woman appeals to her man to proactively help her to respond to him. "Come walk with me," implies that he stays with her for a while until she is given over completely to him. And "make my garden breathe out fragrance" implies that he is the one who must do something to make her garden breathe out fragrance. She needs him to arouse her so that she can respond to him.

Some women find it difficult to respond sensuously to their husbands because they have always thought of sex as fleshly and not spiritual. For example, Galatians 5:19 NASB reads, *"Now the deeds of the flesh are evident, which are: immorality, impurity, sensuality…"* and perhaps you've equated sensuality with *all* sex, and don't feel the freedom to feel sensual toward your husband. You should know that this verse is not addressing sex in the context of marriage. (Other versions of the Bible translate the same word as debauchery, cheap sex, or lustful pleasure.) In chapter 5, Paul is speaking about our sinful nature and what the sinful nature craves. It is not sinful to desire your husband or for him to desire you.

God designed sex for pleasure. In Proverbs he encourages men to enjoy this pleasure exclusively with their wives. *"Drink water from your own well– share your love only with your wife."* Prov 5:15 NLT. Look up several different translations of Prov 5:15 and write down your favorite in the lines below.

_____

_____

_____

Don't you think the imagery of water satisfying our thirst is a passionate description of sex? God is saying that when you are thirsty, you have one well to drink from. He goes on to tell men, *"Let your wife be a fountain of blessing for you. Rejoice in the wife of your youth."* Prov 5:18 NLT

God intended that a husband and wife would turn to and satisfy each other and no one else. Considering this verse, what are some ways you can be a fountain of blessing for your husband?

_____

_____

_____

What are some of the ways that your husband is a blessing to you?

_____

_____

_____

The Hebrew word for sexual intercourse is "to know." Consider Gen 4:1 and write it on the lines below.

_____

_____

_____

To know implies a depth of understanding, and sex provides a place where we experience our husband in a private place intended only for us. Sex brings an intimate knowledge of one another. We can only know each other to the degree that we open up and share ourselves with our spouse. Usually the longer you know someone, the better you really know them. The same generally applies to our sex lives, too. The longer we are married and have sex together, the deeper our knowledge and intimacy with one another grows.

In *Hey Beginner Wife*, I encouraged you with practical suggestions. Consider the following and write down three suggestions you'd like to incorporate in your marriage in the coming months.

- Not to expect that your spouse will know how to meet your sexual needs
- To have vulnerable conversations
- To read a book about married sex that will give you both the words you need to talk about your sex life
- To share what you like and don't like with one another To be open to quickies
- To be mindful about how both of you respond when the other asks for sex
- To be on the alert for selfishness encroaching on your sex life
- To both give and receive
- To assume the best about your husband
- To encourage him about what he's doing well

_____

_____

_____

_____

_____

_____

On a practical note, I mention in *Hey Beginner Wife* that there will be times (whether physical or emotional) when you just don't "feel" like having sex.

Expressions of sexuality around us vary from women flaunting their libido and sharing their stories to anyone who will listen, to the women who aren't comfortable talking about their sexuality with their own husbands. I recognize that each woman and her husband bring a unique experience to the bedroom. At the end of the day, you may still want to sit down one-on-one with a therapist to discuss your experience. And that is okay, in fact it is precisely why we have therapists. *If you feel stuck, it's okay to seek the help of a therapist.* Therapists are there to help you enjoy the fullness of the intimate connection and sexual blessings God intended for you and your husband.

Before I married, no one told me that there would be so many emotions involved in learning how to navigate our sexuality. And who do you talk to as a young bride when you're not sure if it's normal to cry after sex, or wonder why you don't want to have sex every day anymore? Just as your marriage has seasons, your sex life will have seasons, too. You'll have the lacy teddies, but you'll also have the cozy flannels. You'll have the quickies, and you'll also discover that intimacy and satisfaction continue to grow over time. Please don't be too hard on yourself or your husband. Don't give up. This is a gift worth fighting for!

> *Lord, my sex life is important to me. I know it is important to my husband, too. I now see a little bit more how sex was intended to be a beautiful gift from you. I haven't fully experienced this yet, but I am asking you to do what only you can do, and bless our sex life. Please show us how to love one another well, how to learn what blesses each other, knowing this journey is a life-long journey. Help my husband and me to cultivate a heart of gratitude for one another, and teach us how to speak gently and sensitively to each other about our vulnerable places.*

CHAPTER NINE

Forgiveness

Conversation: Heart to Heart

This subject might be a challenging topic for you. If so, I understand. It hasn't always been easy for me, either. I wasn't raised to apologize and work out forgiveness with my parents or siblings, so I didn't have much practice with this when I married. My family might have said, "I'm sorry," but we didn't go beyond that. Maybe that was your experience too? Now, as an adult, you can probably express how difficult it feels to apologize, but that doesn't make it any easier. Your past experience with apologizing will certainly affect your reaction to the whole concept.

I have come to embrace complete apologies as a gift that restores a broken relationship. In fact, I don't know how couples do marriage without extending forgiveness to one another. How do they ever truly restore their relationship after they've wronged or offended one another? Forgiveness is powerful because it can restore a relationship that would otherwise be forever tainted with bitterness.

Apologizing isn't always easy. Our natural inclination is to hide our mistakes and avoid taking responsibility for our actions. Sometimes, we do this to shield ourselves from embarrassment or criticism. Other times, admitting wrongdoing is challenging because we believe our intentions were good, so it's difficult to accept that our actions could be perceived differently.

Application: Putting Love Into Action

What has your experience been with apologizing? If it's been difficult, what has made it difficult for you?

_____

_____

When we married, I was afraid that an apology would open me up to a scathing rebuke. I feared that if I admitted that I had done something wrong, I would then have to endure a lecture that further outlined my faults and berated me. It felt like apologizing would make everything worse for me. I already felt bad, why would I want to feel even worse? Whereas, if I glossed over it, maybe the other person would forget it and all of my discomfort would go away.

Has the fear of correction ever kept you from apologizing?

_____

_____

Would you say that you have any fears about apologizing?

_____

_____

Do you hesitate to apologize because of a specific past experience, or is your fear more about the possibility of what might happen? Check one:

_____I hesitate because of a past experience.

_____I hesitate because of what might happen.

The longer I was married to Steve, the more I realized he didn't try to make me feel horrible after I apologized. He didn't say, "I told you so," or dwell on it. He simply accepted my apology and moved forward. Gradually, it became easier for me. Then one day, I found myself in a similar situation with my preteen daughter. She had a meltdown and screamed at me. After she calmed down, I could sense she wanted to apologize, but instead, she stumbled through various justifications for her outburst. I wish she would have skipped the excuses and simply said, "I'm sorry, Mom," but I remembered being her age and I understood why she reacted the way she did.

While I listened to my daughter, it dawned on me that my husband must have felt the same way in the early years of our marriage when I stumbled through my apologies. He didn't need my excuses. He needed me to say I was sorry and ask him to forgive me. It took me a while, but I eventually trusted him enough to let my guard down and admit when I was wrong. Years later, my daughter learned to let go of her excuses, too.

Inspiration: God's Truth

Choosing to forgive someone is the most generous gift you can give to them. Nowhere is this seen more clearly than in our relationship with the God who created us and gave us ten rules for living well. We call these rules the Ten Commandments. We can choose to obey the rules or not, but when we break one of the rules, God calls it sin and the assigned penalty is separation from him.

The fact that we even have the option to break one of God's rules is pretty amazing to me. We have this option because God gave us the freedom to choose how to live our lives. He didn't create us like robots who were programmed to be his friends, he gave us the *choice*. We can choose to honor God, or choose to live without honoring him. If we choose to honor God, we have to acknowledge that we haven't followed his rules and ask him to forgive us for rejecting him and his rules.

However, then we discover that the penalty for our sin isn't so easily remedied. Our separation from God is an eternal separation. Yes, we are separated from him here on earth, and that separation is set to continue even after we die. A sacrificial death of someone (Jesus) who didn't deserve it (because he never sinned) is the only thing that can absolve sin. Remarkably, Jesus stepped in and took the penalty for us by dying as a proxy for us. Jesus then acts as an intermediary between us and God. If we ask Jesus to forgive us of our sins so that we are no longer separated from God, he will do just that and restore our relationship with God.

How would you describe sin?

_____

_____

Read James 2:8-13 and 1 John 3:4 and write down how the Bible describes sin.

_____

_____

We sin against God. Did you know that we can also sin against each other? Calling our offenses sins makes it sound more serious. Can you think of one or two ways you've sinned against your husband in the last week?

_____

_____

By calling your actions sins, does it change the way you feel about accepting responsibility for what you've done?

_____

_____

Once we recognize our sin, God doesn't ask us to berate ourselves and feel terrible. He wants us to turn toward him and apologize (the biblical word is repent) for our sins so he can forgive us, restore the relationship between us, and we can move on. Acts 3:19 records what happens after we turn to God and repent.

"Repent, then, and turn to God, so that your sins may be wiped out, that times of refreshing may come from the Lord." Acts 3:19 NIV

When we turn toward God with our repentance, our sins will be

_____ out, and times of _____ will come from the Lord. Isn't that amazing? We come to him with our repentance and he rewards us with refreshing!

This can also be true of our relationship with our husband! Knowing that refreshing is on the other side of apologizing to my husband and asking him to forgive me makes me much quicker to apologize. If you haven't experienced this yet with your husband, perhaps looking at it from this angle will help you. Or maybe you want to pray that God would prepare your husband's heart for this whole idea of apologizing and forgiving each other? He may not be ready for it yet. But if *you* are ready, you can begin apologizing to your husband now. If he's uncomfortable that you're asking him to forgive you, it's okay to change your phrasing. Saying "Can we please put this behind us?" works, too.

Application: Putting Love Into Action

If you have experienced forgiveness from Jesus, then you must know the amazing relief that comes with being forgiven and the thanksgiving that wells up in your heart. Once you have experienced forgiveness like that, you can generously extend it to others, especially your spouse. The extent to which you can genuinely apologize and truly forgive is the extent to which you will be happy in your marriage. Since getting this right is important, let's talk about apologies and forgiveness in marriage.

Let's review the three steps of a thorough apology outlined in *Hey Beginner Wife*:

1. Apologize for what you did wrong and actually use the word 'sorry'.
2. Admit and acknowledge that what you did was wrong.
3. Ask for forgiveness.

First we apologize and express remorse. That's why we say, "I'm sorry" and not something casual like, "my bad." Then we admit that we know what we did was wrong. If we leave this part out, our spouse might question if we really understood that we hurt them. It also forces us to really consider what happened. If we simply say, "I'm sorry that you got your feelings hurt. Will you forgive me?" We aren't taking any responsibility for our role in what happened. Acknowledging that what we did was wrong makes the other person feel seen and loved. It also assures them that we are taking responsibility for our role in what happened. Finally we ask if they will forgive us. This is the question that brings closure and moves the ball to their court. If they say yes, they will forgive us, then this restores our relationship. If they don't, we need to pray that God will move on their heart to accept our forgiveness.

Here's an example of a thorough apology:

1. I'm sorry that I snapped.
2. I was wrong to accuse you of doing that on purpose.
3. Would you please forgive me?

Though it might seem like overkill, offering specific information when you apologize is what really gives them power. Let's say that you accused your husband of losing a receipt on purpose, and then went on to say that it was a perfect example of how unreliable he is. Using the template, what would your apology sound like?

1. _____

2. _____

3. _____

When you've wronged your spouse, you must be intentional about apologizing. This is an investment in your relationship and in your marriage. You may have grown up without intentional apologies, and think that thorough apologies like this are overkill, but the two of you should give them a try even before you are married. I think you will quickly appreciate how restorative a thorough apology can be.

When I ask Steve to forgive me, he answers, "Yes, I forgive you." He doesn't answer with, "Don't worry about it," or, "No need to apologize." Those answers don't bring closure or a fresh start. Simply saying, "Yes, I forgive you," puts us on track to starting over. You and your spouse will probably need a little practice before you start to feel comfortable with apologies. That's okay. Keep working at it and you'll get to the place where you can't imagine a marriage without them.

This is not the time to offer excuses for what happened. When you apologize, make it your goal to keep the focus on *your* actions. You will want to say, "I was wrong, but you shouldn't have done that in the first place!" Or you'll want to preface your apology with, "You made me so angry, but I was wrong to say that." Don't do it!

Whose actions should you focus on when apologizing?

_____

As a parent who raised six children, I can tell you that making excuses comes naturally to all of us, and it is something you will probably need to work on, too. Over and over again when we'd pull one child aside to correct them, they would say, "But *he did it first!*" And we'd answer, "Yes, he is responsible for himself and what he did. We will talk to him next, but right now w*e are talking to you.* You are responsible for yourself."

In the same way, you are accountable for your actions and God will hold your husband accountable for his actions. There will be times when your husband doesn't see that what he did was wrong. Take this up with the Lord in prayer. Ask him to change your husband's heart.

Once you've apologized, it's time to move on and receive forgiveness. The Bible tells us in Psalm 103:12 that God removes our sins as far as east is from west. East never touches west. They are polar opposites. God radically removes our sin and moves on. We are to do the same. Once a sin has been repented of, it is not our place to bring it up again. As a couple, I challenge you to hold yourselves to the same standard. When you are upset with one another *do not bring up past offenses.*

Are you easily offended by your husband? Circle YES or NO.

When you and your husband are upset with each other, do you bring up past offenses? If so, are there specific past offenses that you are holding against your husband? Take a few minutes and ask the Holy Spirit to help you lay them down, never to be picked up and

used against your husband again. Write any offense down that you
need to give to Jesus.

_____

_____

_____

_____

Inspiration: God's Truth

Just as God doesn't remind us of sins we have repented of, that
is our example. Be gentle with one another and generous in your
forgiveness. It's challenging to respond to an offense with
forgiveness, but we have been graciously forgiven by Jesus. After
being forgiven of our sins, who are we to deny forgiveness to
someone else? We are called to six different responses.

*"Be gentle and humble, unoffendable in your patience for
others. Tolerate the weaknesses of those in the family of faith,
forgiving one another in the same way you have been graciously
forgiven by Jesus Christ." Col 3:12-13 TPT*

Be _____ and _____,

_____ in your _____

for others. _____ the weaknesses of those in the

family of faith, _____ one another in the same way
you have been graciously forgiven by Jesus Christ. Col 3:12-13 TPT

We're all on a journey of learning how to extend forgiveness. It's important to remember that forgiveness is a process, a choice we make repeatedly, every day, until we're liberated from hurt and our hearts are no longer offended. You already know what you're grappling with. Why not invite the Lord into this space with a simple prayer, asking him to meet you where you are and help you grow in this area? Take a moment to recognize and thank God for his forgiveness towards you. Embracing his love and forgiveness will soften your heart towards forgiving your husband. And just as astounding, forgiveness, as the ultimate act of love, will foster a beautiful and secure intimacy within your marriage.

CHAPTER TEN

Selflessness

Conversation: Heart to Heart

Chapter ten begins with the story of what our life looked like after the earthquake hit.

I wonder what you thought when you read this:

> *"In the (aftermath of the earthquake,) Steve and I didn't question whether or not we were happy. I never once considered my happiness. I never questioned whether I wanted to live like this with him, or leave the marriage and its new financial stress and take the children to live with my parents. Steve and I had committed we would love and cherish each other no matter what, and our mutual purpose of raising a family had not changed. We were simply in a tough season. It was what it was." HBW, Chapter two*

What did you feel when you first read the paragraph above? Did you find it hard to believe that we never questioned our happiness? Write your initial authentic emotions below:

_____

Why did you feel what you felt? Did you agree with my response to the disaster or think I was being super spiritual? If you felt frustrated, or even irritated, take a minute to probe your heart. Is there unbelief there that God can give you the grace to change your perspective on being absolutely resolved in tough seasons? Take a minute and put down your thoughts honestly. (I'm proud of you for being authentically vulnerable with yourself and God.)

_____

_____

_____

Being honest with ourselves is imperative to building a solid foundation for tough seasons.

Application: Putting Love Into Action

When marriages are challenged by hardship, there are usually two choices.

> *"In this season, we could either **turn to** one another and cling to our marriage/friendship for dear life, or we could **turn on** each other and selfISHly seek a way out, even if it meant leaving the other behind. Thankfully, we had the foresight to understand that complaining would only tear down our marriage and not offer a solution or any comfort. Instead of focusing on our hardship, we chose to keep our eyes on our mutual goal of raising children who would change the world one day." HBW Chapter two*

What two choices did we have in this season?

_____

_____

_____

In the midst of hardship, we choose our response. We choose what to focus on, and how we are going to respond to the challenge. Referencing the above paragraphs, what did Steve and I choose to focus on after the earthquake?

_____

_____

_____

If you and your husband experienced a hardship like this, what do you think you would focus on to help you keep your perspective?

_____

_____

_____

Our response to the earthquake and the subsequent daily stress on our marriage and family was grounded in our Christian faith. When the earth stopped shaking, we jumped out of bed to check on our children. Steve scooped up the two little boys, and I gathered the two little girls from their bedroom and we met back on our bed. Before we did anything else, we thanked God for our safety! The children and I stayed on the bed for a few hours while Steve ensured that the living room was free of broken glass, and he had picked up everything that had been strewn across the room to prepare a safe place for the kids to move around. As the sun rose, we could see the damage in our neighborhood. We checked on our neighbors. And again, we marveled at our safety.

In the coming weeks, we prayed and asked God for strength. Steve and I were both emotionally tired. It was immediately apparent that the earthquake would affect his business, and the financial repercussions happened quickly. But because our trust was in God and his provision and his sovereignty, we didn't *turn on each other*. We *turned toward God* and his promise to provide for us, his people.

When I struggled with our circumstances, I didn't blame Steve. I looked to God to provide for us. All of this wasn't Steve's fault. Why would I blame him? Why would I get mad at him? Why would I complain to him? I took all the emotion I had and directed it toward God. What might have looked like a selfLESS response to others, *was actually a response of trusting God to meet us in this difficult place.*

Many times when trials come, we are selfISHly tempted to blame, become angry, or complain. Have you walked through a difficult experience that challenged your selfISHness? Write it below:

_____

_____

_____

Inspiration: God's Truth

Let's look at what God's word says about complaining. Read Philippians 2:14-15 TLB:

"In everything you do, stay away from complaining and arguing so that no one can speak a word of blame against you. You are to live clean, innocent lives as children of God in a dark world full of people who are crooked and stubborn. Shine out among them like beacon lights, holding out to them the word of life."

In the midst of a crisis, how can you keep from complaining, blaming or getting angry with your husband? It sometimes seems impossible, yet because we have made a covenant vow in our marriage, we can go back to what phrase of our wedding vows?

_____

_____

_____

Another thing that helped us to respond to the stress of the earthquake was the thorough understanding that we had made a promise to each other to stay together "for better, for worse." The idea that either of us would walk away from the marriage because things got difficult never crossed our minds. In the purest sense of the words, covenants require *that we rise up and do hard things to sustain the commitment we made*, while a marriage contract allows for a way out.

We have a choice to CHOOSE to do it God's way and trust him to be faithful! A lifelong covenant marriage is the walking out of our vows to stay together for better for worse, for richer, for poorer, in sickness, and in health. This takes a selfLESSness that goes against our natural bent to be selfISH. As much as I've thought about this, I don't think there is any way to overcome our selfISHness without recognizing it for what it is. SelfISHness is sin. SelfISHness puts our needs first, above those of any other. SelfISHness is a decision that defies God's command to love him with our whole heart and to love our neighbor as ourselves. The only way to do that is to recognize that *in and of ourselves*, we cannot love in this way

Philippians 2:3 TLB says, *"Don't be selfish; don't live to make a good impression on others. Be humble, thinking of others as better than yourself."*

We NEED the power of the Holy Spirit to walk in

_____love!

If you've tried to love others in your own strength, you know how difficult it is when they are unlovable, hurtful, selfISH, or stubborn. Your fond feelings of love start to erode, and you eventually retreat and move away from one another.

Recognizing that we are to obey God's command to love him first and foremost helps to put things in perspective. One of the religious people of the day asked Jesus this question, *"Teacher, which is the great commandment in the Law?" And he said to him, "You shall love the Lord your God with all your heart, and with all your soul, and with all your mind." This is the great and foremost commandment. The second is similar: "You shall love your neighbor as yourself." Mt 22:36-40 NASB*

What did Jesus say were the two greatest commandments?

1. _____

2. _____

Today, many books and speakers emphasize the importance of loving ourselves. You'll notice that sometimes the message to love yourself often sounds like protective selfishness. However, we *are* to love ourselves because of Christ's love. In John 15:9, Jesus says, "*As the Father has loved me, so have I loved you.*" This is the secret! We must RECEIVE God's love in order to love ourselves! Then we will be able to love others...including our husband!

In Matthew 22:39, Jesus says to love your neighbor (which includes your husband) as yourself. What does it mean to love your husband as yourself?

_____

_____

_____

When you think of loving your husband as yourself, what comes to mind?

_____

_____

_____

Referencing the entire fifth chapter of Ephesians, Bible teacher Tim Keller teaches that marriage only works "to the degree that it approximates the pattern of God's self-giving love in Christ…Start here, Paul says. Do for your spouse what God did for you in Jesus, and the rest will follow."[3]

"Be imitators of God in everything you do, for then you will represent your father as his beloved sons and daughters. And continue to walk surrendered to the extravagant love of Christ, for he surrendered his life as a sacrifice for us." Eph 5:1-2a TPT

Rewrite this verse as if it were your assignment for the upcoming week:

_____

_____

Now read Philippians 2:3 again. Can you imagine a successful marriage where one or both partners choose selfISHness? It's easy to immediately think of ways your husband is selfish towards you, but how can YOU choose to be selfLESS towards your husband? Write down two practical ways:

1. _____

2. _____

3   Timothy Keller, *The Meaning of Marriage,* (New York: Riverhead Books, 2011) *43.*

Why do you think Jesus wants us to choose selfLESSness?

_____

_____

_____

In the oft-quoted biblical definition of love found in 1 Corinthians, God says that love is not self-seeking. *"Love is patient, love is kind. It does not envy, it does not boast, it is not proud. It does not dishonor others, it is not self-seeking, it is not easily angered, it keeps no record of wrongs."* 1 Cor 13: 4-5 NIV But we all know that loving selfLESSly and putting the interests of others above ourselves for any length of time is hard. How can we actually do this?

We find the answer in Philippians 4:13 NASB, *"I can do all things through him (Christ) who strengthens me."* It is only a relationship with Christ and a continual refilling of his love that enables us to generously love our spouse selfLESSly. Knowing that Christ will strengthen you and help you love selfLESSly, do you want to ask him to help you do that? Thinking of a difficult challenge that faces you, fill in the blank below and make it a prayer.

Paul said "I can do all things through Christ who strengthens me." Jesus, I would like to be able to boldly proclaim that with your

help   and   your   strength,   I   can   _____

_____through

Christ who strengthens me.

Sometimes choosing selfLESSness is difficult, but in Christ, we can pray that he helps us to become more like him. Since you've been married, have you become more aware of your selfISHness? (Circle Yes or No)

YES	NO

Tim Keller wrote, "The gospel is this: We are more sinful and flawed in ourselves than we ever dared believe, yet at the very same time we are more loved and accepted in Jesus Christ than we ever dared hope. This is the only kind of relationship that will really transform us."[4]

Do you see your selfISHness as sin? That might sound harsh, but acknowledging selfISHness as sin will help us become more like Jesus.

_____

_____

Considering what you know of Jesus, do you see selfISHness in his life?

_____

The Bible is filled with direction for how we are to treat one another. The Greek phrase 'one another' appears 100 times in the New Testament. Since the translations read 'one another,' it's easy to think of everyone else *except our husband* when we read these

---

4   Timothy Keller, *The Meaning of Marriage,* (New York: Riverhead Books, 2011) *44.*

verses. But of course these verses are meant to instruct us in every relationship, and especially our marriage relationship.

"Be devoted to one another in brotherly love; give preference to one another in honor." Rom 12:10 NASB. What would it mean to give preference to your husband?

Husbands are told to "love your wives just as Christ loved the church and gave himself up for her." According to this verse, how is your husband commanded to express his love to you?

The tendency after reading this verse could be to focus on how your husband is not loving you as Christ loved the church. Let's focus on ways you DO see your husband loving you like Christ loved the church. Write them below:

(If your husband is not a Christ follower, or you only see his selfISHness, refuse to be offended and ask the Holy Spirit to meet your husband exactly where he is.)

Do you trust that if you love your husband selfLESSly, he will love you in the same way? If not, please take this to prayer. Pray that God does a work in your heart, and in your husband's heart, to become more and more like Jesus. Take a minute and rewrite John 15:12-13 in your own words, inserting your name and your husband's name into your version.

"This is my commandment: Love each other in the same way I have loved you. There is no greater love than to lay down one's life for one's friends." John 15:12-13 NLT

_____

_____

What does it mean to lay down your life?

_____

_____

Laying down your selfISHness to serve your husband (and others) is humbling. Look at what Jesus says about those who serve.

"The greatest among you shall be your servant." Matthew 23:11 ESV

It takes humility to serve others. Even if you're serving someone you love, we often wrestle with an inner voice that demands that we be the one being served. In many societies, having a servant is a marker of success. We've come to believe that only the wealthy, the famous, or the successful have servants. But in God's economy, the successful ones are the ones who choose to serve others.

Can you think of someone whose example of serving you admire?

_____

_____

How do you respond to the inner voice that tells you not to serve?

Living selfLESSly in marriage is countercultural, but Christlike. While choosing selfLESSness is a daily challenge, be assured that it does not go unnoticed. Jesus promised that *"your father in the secret place is the one who is watching all that you do in secret and will continue to reward you openly."* Mt 6:18 TPT

Jesus' promise applies to you, too. Our choices to clean up someone else's mess and not complain about it is something no one else sees, and it is selfLESS. In marriage we routinely have the opportunity to clean up after our husbands, some of us more than others. For some it means picking up their dirty socks, and for some it's not so much cleaning up after their husbands as it is proactively serving them: choosing to do a load of laundry even when you're tired because you know that he cannot get to it before his business trip, or offering to run an errand he hates to do. What are you doing in secret? Write out the promise to you from Matthew 6:18 below.

Just as you have a choice to choose to welcome God into your marriage by inviting him into your marriage covenant, you have a choice to choose selfLESSness. People who operate selfLESSly in marriage *don't think less of themselves, they just think of themselves less and put their spouse first.* God is not asking you to make a choice between fulfillment and sacrifice. He is offering you mutual fulfillment through mutual sacrifice. Surprisingly, when we love our spouse sacrificially, we experience deep happiness. We tap into imitating God and his nature, and we discover his happiness in loving others.

As you consider choosing selfLESSness, take a minute to include God in your commitment to this choice. Through prayer, invite him to transform you to be more like Jesus and learn what it means to love your husband as yourself, and to lay your life down for your husband. Make a declaration of faith by filling in the blanks below and reading it over yourself.

God, I thank you for selfLESSly laying down your life for me. I desire to be more like you. I repent and ask you to forgive

_____ in my life. Thank you Holy Spirit for

empowering me to _____ in my marriage. In Jesus' name, Amen.

CHAPTER ELEVEN

Cheerfulness

Conversation: Heart to Heart

"If mama ain't happy, ain't nobody happy." Have you ever heard this quote? I've seen it on plaques meant for hanging in the kitchen, and I've seen it embroidered on pillows, but I cannot imagine Abigail Adams, Clara Barton, Harriet Tubman, Eleanor Roosevelt, or Rosa Parks–women I admire–bringing this sentiment into their homes.

Remarkable women are not complainers, nor do they put the burden of their happiness on others. Think about it, are you entitled to make everyone else's life miserable if you're unhappy? You're far enough into this book to notice a pattern – our decisions matter. You have the power to change your perspective and, in the process, change your attitude. When tempted to complain, choosing gratitude will give you the power to overcome that temptation.

As a woman, you have a remarkable influence on the climate in your home. Typically, if you are unhappy, everyone in the home is affected. However, this does not mean that your husband and children are required to contribute to *your* happiness. It is *our* responsibility to *choose* happiness and set an example in our homes.

Application: Putting Love Into Action

Have you ever used the quote "If mama ain't happy, ain't nobody happy?" Or, "Happy Wife, Happy Life?" If so, when you think back on it, what emotion were you feeling when you did?

_____

_____

Maybe you were feeling unappreciated, or maybe a bit sassy? Did you use it as a way to complain? On that note, do you find yourself complaining in your home? Trust me, it is easy to do! Think of a time you complained in your home and write it below:

_____

_____

Now take a minute to flip the script on that complaint and write down something you could be grateful for in that situation.

_____

_____

Do you depend on your husband or children to make you happy?

Yes

No

Why or why not? Be honest here. Honesty will allow you to make the change so that you can set the climate and tone in your home.

_____

_____

Conversation: Heart to Heart

When I had my first three children, I remember consciously deciding not to yell at them when upset. I thought, "I'm an adult, and they are watching me. It's my job to exhibit steady self-control. If I need to correct them, it will be more effective if I do not yell at them." And then our family vacationed with another young family whose mother had not made this resolution. Her children were energetic and happy, and I thought she and her husband were doing a great job of parenting, but on this vacation, I observed her angrily screaming at her children multiple times a day. "Why does she allow herself to do this?" I silently questioned. Granted, it's a lot easier to yell when you're upset, and at times, exercising self-control not to lose my temper exhausted me. But if *she (a godly, admirable woman who volunteers countless hours, is consistently cheerful outside the house, and even leads Bible studies)* is yelling at her kids, I wondered if I could relax and allow myself to yell sometimes.

I am embarrassed to say that I came to that conclusion and, in the following weeks, permitted myself to lose my temper. And you know what? It felt so good just to let loose and scream a few times. The kids had gotten on my last nerve, so I could justify it, right? Only, I couldn't justify it. After losing my temper for the first time,

I felt terrible but I kept going. Then I discovered that having consciously pushed self-control aside for several weeks; it now took some real effort to reign it back in, rise above my feelings, and do the right thing. But that is exactly what I needed to do. I started by apologizing to my children for losing my control. I told them I was wrong and asked them to forgive me multiple times as I tried to break my new habit.

Application: Putting Love Into Action

When you lose your temper, do you yell at your children (or your husband)? If so, what are things that trigger your yelling? Write them below and ask the Holy Spirit to help you walk in self-control.

_____

_____

I think sometimes we justify our lack of self-control because we are tired, have too much on our plate or our kids are driving us crazy. But, I couldn't blame my children for my poor behavior. My behavior was my responsibility, and thankfully, I got it back under control. This is exactly what made women of old so strong and powerful. Despite their circumstances, they did not blame others for their poor behavior. They chose to do the right thing because it was the right thing to do.

When your emotions take you in the wrong direction, stop and identify your inner narrative. What are you telling yourself right now? Oftentimes we don't stop to consider the worthiness of our thoughts. Instead, we simply give in to them and are led by our feelings and our emotions. There's another way.

Inspiration: God's Truth

"For though we walk in the flesh, we are not waging war according to the flesh. For the weapons of our warfare are not of the flesh but have divine power to destroy strongholds. <u>We destroy arguments and every lofty opinion raised</u> against the knowledge of God, and take every thought captive to obey Christ." 1 Cor 10:3-5 ESV

We are human, and at the same time, we are spiritual beings who live in a spiritual world that we cannot see. As a result, we experience spiritual attacks that must be resisted using spiritual wisdom and weapons. Sometimes, these attacks take the form of thoughts and arguments that we dwell on and seriously consider as truth. If we are not spiritually aware of the battle in our minds, we may fail to recognize that we first spent time meditating on our husband's shortcomings, both overarching weaknesses that he brought into the marriage and his most recent misstep that 'ruined' our morning, leading us to a place of disgruntled irritation. Subsequently, we find ourselves snapping at him for minor things such as not closing the milk carton or leaving his wallet on the bathroom counter. Our thoughts precede our actions, paving the way for us to react angrily to our husbands at the slightest provocation.

When we discover that this is happening, it's time to consider whether our thoughts are to blame.

"We use God's mighty weapons, not worldly weapons, to <u>knock down the strongholds of human reasoning and to destroy false arguments.</u>" 1 Cor 10:4 NLT

In 1 Corinthians 10, Paul writes about using God's mighty weapons to wage war. Consider the underlined phrases in the two scriptures above and write down what we are warring against.

_____

_____

_____

In 1 Corinthians 10:5, Paul exhorts us to take every thought captive. In other words, don't simply allow your mind to freely dwell on your lofty opinions of other people, or the false arguments you've crafted in your mind against your husband. Instead, take every thought **captive**. A *captive* is someone (or something) taken and held as a prisoner of war. Captives are kept within bounds, confined to a specific holding cell as punishment. To take your thoughts captive is to capture a thought and forcibly overpower it in such a way that it no longer takes preeminence in your mind. You forcibly deconstruct the thought with truth and choose to overcome its power with a new perspective.

Your thoughts are the battleground for lies and accusations, and if they go unchecked your actions and attitudes will simply follow along like a whipped animal. In order to win the war for cheerfulness in your home, you must consider the war waging in your thoughts and fight back.

<u>We destroy arguments and every lofty opinion raised</u> against the knowledge of God, and take every thought captive to obey Christ." 1 Cor 10:3-5 ESV

Take a moment to think of an argument or lofty opinion that you've recently entertained in your mind against someone else. Write it below.

_____

_____

Now, stop to consider how you could have taken that thought captive. What is the truth about that thought?

_____

_____

Because you gave that thought preeminence in your mind, what happened? How did it affect your behavior? How did it negatively impact your relationship with your husband?

_____

_____

Looking back, can you recognize the battle that went on in your mind? Does it make sense to you that Paul described this as warfare in 1 Corinthians 10:3?

_____

_____

As much as our thoughts influence our attitudes and actions, what we carry in our heart does as well. The Bible teaches about the importance of guarding our hearts.

"Watch over your heart with all diligence, for from it flow the springs of life." Prov 4:23 NASB

"Above all else, guard your heart, for everything you do flows from it." Prov 4:23 NIV

"Guard your heart above all else, for it determines the course of your life." Prov 4:23 NLT

"So above all, guard the affections of your heart, for they affect all that you are. Pay attention to the welfare of your innermost being, for from there flows the wellspring of life." Prov 4:23 TPT

Underline the words in Proverbs 4:23 that best explain to you the reason why God teaches us to guard our hearts. In the lines below, rewrite the verse as a directive to yourself.

_____

_____

In Psalms we learn that our speech is affected by the condition of our heart. Look up Psalm 16:8-9a and write down how the psalmist explains that he acquired a glad heart and the rejoicing that came with it.

_____

_____

With the deep assurance that the Lord is always with us comes a glad and happy heart. The NIV states, *"With him at my right hand, I will not be shaken. Therefore my heart is glad and my tongue rejoices."* Have you ever read through the Psalms? Over and over again, the writers meditate on the nearness of God, how God protects us and provides for us, of his kindness toward us, and his commitment to never leave us. Read through Psalm 145:8-20 in your Bible and look for a verse that makes your heart glad. Write the verse below and commit to thinking about it every day this week. When you're tempted to dwell on something negative, replace it with the verse you chose to remind you of what God will do for you.

_____

_____

_____

_____

Application: Putting Love Into Action

Cheerfulness is a choice that becomes a habit. In the same way, complaining is a choice that becomes a habit. If you've recognized a predisposition to complain but would like to become a cheerful woman, taking control of your thoughts is huge! In *Hey Beginner Wife*, I covered some things that are enemies of a cheerful spirit. Critical complaining, venting, jealousy, and comparison will rob you of joy.

If you will recognize these things as enemies to your marriage you will be ahead of the game. Let's consider how each one can do damage. Think of a time in your marriage, or the marriage of someone you know, and write down an example of the behavior, and then the damage that these enemies did to the marriage.

Critical complaining

_____

_____

Venting

_____

_____

Jealousy/Envy

_____

_____

Comparison

_____

_____

As you ask the Holy Spirit to help you, and do everything in your power to be cheerful, resist the urge to wonder if you made a mistake by marrying your partner. Remember that there is no such thing as a perfect spouse. Comparison is so sneaky that we often don't recognize that we are doing it until our cheerfulness is stolen from us! Just as you are not perfect, your husband isn't either; and that is true for every couple you know. Happy couples choose to believe the best about one another. No one else will hear your inner dialogue, and no one else has the power to take control of your inner dialogue when it goes to a negative place except you.

Now that you are aware that you are in a spiritual battle, start storing the truth of God's word in your heart. This will help you fight mental accusations against your husband with the truth of God's word. A cheerful and happy marriage begins when you take control of your thoughts and steer them in the right direction. You've got this! Remember, the cheerfulness you cultivate in your heart can set the tone and atmosphere in your home and empower you to overcome challenges with grace and love.

CHAPTER TWELVE

Expectations

Conversation: Heart to Heart

We weren't even married yet when Steve took me by surprise and pushed back against one of my long-standing expectations. I had never, not even once, pictured my wedding day without my groom in a black tuxedo. He would wear black and I would wear white. Classic. Striking. When in the long history of traditional, gorgeous weddings had a groom ever worn anything except black?!

And now my fiance was telling me that he had picked out a *light gray* tux.

Um, no.

In one fell swoop, I was certain that he had just ruined our wedding pictures. But he wouldn't back down. "You get to pick your dress, and I get to pick the tuxedo I feel best in. And I feel best in light gray. Light gray is the most flattering of all the colors I tried on."

"But grooms wear black. I have always pictured my groom in black. I really want you to wear black. I don't know what you're talking about. I saw you in black at Dave's wedding and you looked amazing. I'll be the one looking at you. Don't I get to pick what you'll be wearing?"

"Michelle, there's another issue at hand. Our wedding is at 10:30 in the morning and from what I've read, there are morning suits and evening suits. Light gray is also a more appropriate color for a morning wedding."

I must confess that at this point, I did not know where this man came from. Did he *read* this somewhere? What man *reads* about what to wear for his wedding? Mind you, this is before the days of the internet and search engines. Was he actually reading etiquette books or men's fashion magazines?

Steve wouldn't budge. On our wedding day, he and his six groomsmen stood awash in light gray at the altar, and I got over it. It surprised me that he had such a strong opinion about what he wore, but I did agree that it made sense that he should feel his most handsome self at his wedding. I had to recognize that my expectations were about what I envisioned for *my* wedding, and I hadn't considered the opinions of the real-life man I was marrying.

Application: Putting Love Into Action

Have you been married long enough to identify some of the expectations you had about marriage and your husband? We all have these ideas, sometimes without even realizing it, about how our husbands should behave and what chores they should handle.

Name one expectation that surprised you because you didn't realize you held it?

_____

_____

Think about your relationship with your husband. Can you identify an expectation that he completely rejected?

_____

_____

Have you ever found yourself comparing your husband to someone else? Can you recall an expectation that arose from this comparison?

_____

_____

Have there been moments when you felt embarrassed because your husband didn't meet someone else's expectations?

_____

_____

Do you deal with COMPARISON? I think we all do at one point or another.

Growing up, did you ever find yourself questioning your own beauty? I certainly did. During my high school years, magazines were everywhere. Each new issue promised the latest beauty trends, seasonal fashion must-haves, and endless advice on relationships. I would flip through pages filled with airbrushed faces and perfectly styled models, comparing myself and always feeling inadequate. I vividly recall thinking, "If I'm not even the most attractive girl in my graduating class, how could I ever hope to be seen as beautiful in the real world?" It seemed to me that beauty was some kind of accolade you had to earn.

I empathize with the young woman who reached out to me, sharing her frustration about her new husband. She confided that she feels disheartened because "days pass without him telling me that I'm pretty."

I suspect this dear woman longed to feel worthy and questioned her beauty even *before* she married. We all have a similar void unless another has filled it. And the only One who can honestly fill that void is the One who knows us better than we know ourselves. It's our Creator, the One who chose the color of our hair, the shape of our hips, and the length of our legs. He's the One who would never have been satisfied if he hadn't created us. He's the one who looks deep inside our hearts and says, "I like you." Until we know our Creator truly loves us, there will always be a part of us that looks to our husbands to complete us and assuage our insecurities. Once we have embraced and internalized the truth about ourselves as declared by God, we will no longer seek validation from our husbands. Instead, we will come to realize that we are genuinely accepted, loved, and valued every day because it is God who has affirmed our worth and importance.

Inspiration: God's Truth

Have you ever thought about how God deliberately chose all the little details that make you uniquely you? Out of all the genes swirling around in your family tree, he picked out the precise color of your hair, your skin tone, the sound of your voice, and even those hidden talents and skills you possess. It's pretty amazing when you think about it!

What do you think God got exactly right in the way he formed you?

_____

_____

If you're honest, what do you wish God would have done differently when he made you?

_____

_____

As I'm writing this, I can just imagine how hard it was to write down the things you think God got right, and yet how easy it was to list the things you wish he would have done differently! I can relate to that, but what if we change our perspective?

Perhaps not right now, but sometime soon, can you plan to quiet yourself and discuss this with the Lord? Imagine sitting before him and honestly telling him you wish he had made another choice. Then, ask him to reveal to you what he absolutely loves about the way he made you. It may take several quiet sittings to hear his answer, but I believe he would like to reveal that to you.

Take a minute and meditate on the love God has for you! He is crazy about you! Look up Psalm 17:8 and write it in the space below:

_____

_____

In this scripture, the psalmist David was asking God to keep him as the "apple of his eye!" This phrase, which first was used in the Bible, comes from a Hebrew expression that literally means "little man of the eye." It refers to the tiny reflection of yourself that you can see in someone else's pupils. To be the apple of someone's eye means that they are gazing upon you and watching you closely with great affection. Your very image is dancing in the eyes of that person! In modern English, the phrase "apple of my eye" indicates something or someone that you value above all others! And YOU are the apple of God's eye! God absolutely cherishes you beyond measure!

How does it make you feel to think about being the "apple of God's eye"? Is that hard for you to believe? Yes or No? Why or Why not?

_____

_____

Once God shows you his perspective, you will no longer need your husband's affirmation in this area. Your husband is not the one who should define you. As much as I would like my husband to tell me that I'm beautiful, worthy, and he treasures only me, it is far better that my definition of self-worth comes from someone who is not subject to change, world events, or job stress. A confident, mature wife finds her identity in the God who created her. He alone can reveal the truth about who she is and what true success looks like for her.

God's thoughts toward you are always constant and never change. If you can truly understand the depth of God's unwavering love for you, then you won't rely on your husband to validate you. But how do we even begin to comprehend something that feels so ethereal?

It is only by faith that we obtain this confidence. It takes faith to believe what God says about us, and the Bible tells us how we can grow in our faith. The answer is found in Romans 10:17.

Faith comes by _____ and through the

_____ of _____.

Reading and meditating on what the psalmist tells us is true about God and how he feels toward each one of us is a great place to start. Imagine that Psalm 139 was written directly about you. When you read it out loud, it sounds like a conversation that you are having with God. Try reading the next section out loud, and you'll see what I mean.

> *"Lord, you know everything there is to know about me. You perceive every movement of my heart and soul, and you understand my every thought before it even enters my mind. You are SO intimately aware of me, Lord. You read my heart like an open book and you know all the words I'm about to speak before I even start a sentence!" (Psalm 139:1-4a TPT)*
>
> *"This is just TOO WONDERFUL, DEEP, and INCOMPREHENSIBLE! Your understanding of me brings me wonder and strength." (Psalm 139:6 TPT)*
>
> *"You formed my innermost being, shaping my delicate inside and my intricate outside, and wove them all together in my*

mother's womb... It simply amazes me to think about it! You saw who you created me to be before I even became me! Before I'd ever seen the light of day, the number of days you planned for me were already recorded in your book. Every single moment you are thinking of me and you cherish me constantly in your every thought!" (Psalm 139: 13-14,16, 17-18 TPT)

How is it possible that every single moment you are thinking of me? How is it possible that when I awake every morning you are thinking of me? How is it possible that I am not hidden from your sight?! How is it possible that you really thought about me before I was born and watched over every detail to create me just as you planned in your heart?

How is it possible that you love me and care for me this much? It is too wonderful for me. I want to believe it's true but it's so much. Please look down at me and see if there is any path of pain that I'm walking on, and lead me to the glorious path that brings me to you."

(Excerpts and prayer paraphrasing from Psalm 139 TPT)

When a woman truly believes that she is acceptable and worthy in God's eyes, it transforms her. She becomes confident and joyful and doesn't rely on her husband to validate her. Knowing that she is loved and seen by God, she no longer feels the need to pressure her husband for love and affection. In response, this confidence takes the pressure off of him, and he will likely feel even more fondly toward her.

I am not saying that husbands should not express love and affection toward their wives. Far from it! I believe marriage should be filled with affection and outward expressions of love. I'm talking about the inner places of our hearts that long to be loved and accepted, and no matter what our husbands do, we still feel empty. This inner longing is so deep that only the One who created you can satisfy this longing. Only God can truly make you feel loved and accepted. Your husband can contribute to that, but your husband can never satisfy you completely.

Application: Putting Love Into Action

Perhaps you're looking for your husband to fulfill you in ways he was never designed to.

Your Creator determines your true worth, and he thought you were worth dying for. If you've been a Christian for any length of time, you may have heard that often enough that you don't even think about it anymore. But let's pause. Let's think about that. What if someone died to save your life today?

Imagine a scenario where an individual actually gave his/her life for you. What would you feel toward that person?

_____

_____

I'm sure the immense gratitude you would feel towards someone who sacrificed their life for you would be unexplainable. That's the depth of love God has for you—he loved you so much that he gave his only son, Jesus, so that you could have eternal life (John 3:16)!

He didn't just create you; he sees you, treasures you, and loves you unconditionally.

The greatest gift you can receive is his love. In return, giving him your heart in eternal gratitude is the most meaningful response you can offer.

If you find yourself filled with unmet emotional expectations from your husband, shift your focus away from what your husband is not doing and concentrate on what God has already said is true about you and what he has already done for you. Once you grasp how precious you are to God, you'll find a new security and happiness you may not have experienced before. So, if you find yourself frustrated or unhappy with unmet emotional expectations from your husband, shift your focus away from what he isn't doing and instead, concentrate on what God has already spoken over your life and what he's already done for you. When you truly grasp just how cherished you are in his eyes, you'll discover a fresh sense of security and a deeper happiness that you may never have known before.

As we wrap up this chapter, I want to encourage you with a challenge: Take a moment to sit and express gratitude to God for the blessings in your life, especially in your marriage and specifically concerning your husband. Practicing gratitude has a remarkable way of transforming your heart and fostering a beautiful humility.

I invite you to jot down ten things you're thankful for regarding your husband and your marriage. This simple exercise can help you recognize and appreciate the positive aspects of your relationship, reinforcing a sense of appreciation and love.

1. _____

2. _____

3. _____

4. _____

5. _____

6. _____

7. _____

8. _____

9. _____

10. _____

Self-Control

Conversation: Heart to Heart

I just can't seem to keep quiet about where my husband chooses to park the car. It seems to me that he parks as far away from the entrance as he can, and I still don't understand it. Just the other day we arrived at church and there were plenty of parking spots available in the three rows closest to the church doors. He looked down each aisle and kept going. We got to the next to last row and then he decided to back into a spot on the last row! I finally blurted out, "Okay, I did an amazing job of holding my tongue until you decided to back into *the last row!*" I started laughing, and he just smiled at me. This parking saga also happens in the winter when I complain that the weather is preventing me from walking every day. My husband will invariably park further away than I like and tease me with, "But you said you want to get more steps in. I'm just helping you out!" Ha! Clearly, we each make different decisions about where to park our car. After nearly forty years of marriage, you'd think I'd get used to this parking quirk, but nope—it still baffles me. Maybe you and your husband have different preferences as well?

Here's another one of my preferences that you may relate to. I have definite opinions about how to load the dishwasher because I want to fit as much in as I possibly can. When the kids were in high school I even made a diagram to show how to load it, and yet they still took creative license and put things where I didn't think they belonged. I finally had to come to terms with the fact that I didn't want to die on this hill. So I decided to give them the freedom to do it their way (within reason, of course!). What did it really matter if two plates and three mugs didn't fit? There was always next time, right?

Since my husband has started working from home, he loads the dishwasher all day long. The other day I opened it to put away a dirty mug and rearranged the top shelf the way I like it. I saw him in the next room and playfully, and dramatically, exclaimed, "Can you just load the dishwasher the right way?" And with a gleam in his eye, he baited me, "And what way would that be?" "MY WAY!!!" I burst out, unable to keep a straight face. And I just laughed with him because this saga goes on and on, and I finally just came out and said it. I truly believe that my way is the optimal and best way, but I couldn't say it with a straight face because after all these years it really doesn't matter. And you know what, maybe I'm even wrong! After years of arguing about this, it's become funny. It's like we circle each other in the boxing ring making all the same moves, and we just laugh at ourselves.

These examples are simple things, but the point is the same with harder situations in marriage. None of us are perfect and we ALL have our idiosyncrasies. This verse from James 3:2,4 MSG says it so well.

Inspiration: God's Truth

"None of us is perfectly qualified. We get it wrong nearly every time we open our mouths. If you could find someone whose speech

was perfectly true, you'd have a perfect person in perfect control of life. A word out of your mouth may seem of no account, but it can accomplish nearly anything —or destroy it!"

Once you are married, your words and actions will either strengthen your marriage or tear it down. Proverbs 14:1 declares, "The wise woman builds her house, but the foolish woman tears it down with her own hands." When it comes to your marriage and family, will you show yourself to be a wise or a foolish woman? Referencing not only the sound structure of a house but also the spiritual well-being and healthy relationships of the family within, King Solomon stresses in this proverb that a wise woman will consider the foundations of her marriage and family with the future in mind. Her words and actions will be an investment into the house's integrity, or they will contribute to its destruction.

King Solomon wrote, "The wise woman builds her house," and called to mind a picture of a woman literally building her own home, brick by brick. What do you think he meant by this?

_____

_____

"A foolish woman tears it down with her own hands." Give a few examples of how a woman can foolishly destroy her own home.

_____

_____

We might offhandedly call someone wise or a fool, but used in proverbs these words are profound and meant to catch our attention.

It's as if we are given a choice, "Aspire a life of wisdom or foolish-ness." Between the two choices, I hope you will choose wisdom!

But, what if you don't feel wise? What if you've made some foolish choices and are crawling out from underneath them? Read the good news in James 1:5 and write down God's answer to you.

_____

_____

We can literally ASK God for wisdom! I have been praying this prayer and asking God for wisdom since I first heard that he invites us to simply ask. God wants his daughters to be wise. Let's explore a few promises about wisdom.

Proverbs 4:7 Wisdom is supreme, or "the principal thing;"

Therefore _____

_____.

Ecclesiastes 7:12 Wisdom is a _____, *but*

the advantage of knowledge is that wisdom _____

_____.

Proverbs 8:11 For wisdom is _____

_____, *and* _____

_____ *can compare with her.*

Proverbs 31:26 She opens her mouth _____, *and*

the teaching of _____ *is on her tongue.*

Which of these verses resonates most with you as something you'd like to pursue?

_____

_____

Application: Putting Love Into Action

As wise women, we want to build our home and not tear it down. Toward that end, one of the most significant things we can do to build up our home is to speak words of life and encouragement to our husbands. We show ourselves to be wise or foolish based on the words we speak and the words we do not speak. Learning to control our tongues is one of the hardest things we will ever do, but that doesn't mean we shouldn't continue to work on it.

Words are remarkably powerful. We speak so freely that we forget how powerful they are until we are blessed with a profound word of encouragement, or wounded by a piercing word of disdain.

Have you ever stopped to consider how God created the world? Read Genesis 1:3, 1:4, 1:5, 1:6 and you'll see His pattern. God *said*, "Let there be light;" and there was light! God used His *words* and created our world. Stunning! Proverbs tells us that there are two things in the power of our tongue. What are they?

_____

_____

Perhaps you've never stopped to consider the power that your words have. But think back on the last few weeks. Can you recall a time when you said something to your husband that you wish you hadn't said?

_____

_____

What was going on that caused you to say these words? Emotions, frustrating circumstances, disappointments, insecurities? Or something else?

_____

_____

No matter what it was, God still challenges us to gain control of our tongues. One or two words may sound insignificant, but consider what the Bible says in *James 3:5b-6, "It only takes a spark, remember, to set off a forest fire. A careless or wrongly placed word out of your mouth can do that. By our speech, we can ruin the world, turn harmony to chaos, throw mud on a reputation, send the whole world up in smoke, and go up in smoke with it."*

We don't make things better with our careless words, do we? If I rewrite this verse as an exhortation to myself, it's sobering. "Michelle, remember that it only takes a spark to set off a forest fire. In the same way, your careless speech can ruin the evening with your husband. Your words of accusation can turn harmony into chaos. Sharing your husband's weaknesses with your mother can throw mud on his reputation. Continually threatening to leave him when you're upset can ultimately lead to the end of your marriage."

That was dramatic, wasn't it? But no more dramatic than the picture James painted in this verse. Thankfully he also tells us in verse 2 that no one is in perfect control of their tongue. Every one of us, young and old, wise and foolish, is guilty of the same thing. The difference is that some of us discern the importance of fighting the battle and choose to reign in our speech.

One thing that comes up over and over is the tendency to assign blame before we know the whole story. We assume that we know why our husband is late coming home, or didn't do something he'd promised to do. Thinking we have the whole story, we can get all worked up, jump to conclusions, and then unnecessarily accuse him. In these moments I find it very helpful to use self-control and stop to remember that I am married to a good-willed man. I challenge myself to approach the situation with an open heart, and refrain from getting upset until I hear his side of the story.

Have you ever assumed something about your husband only to find out it wasn't true in the end? Circle YES or NO.

If yes, write it below and then the truth about the situation.

_____

_____

I see a pattern that I have had to fight falling into many times in my marriage. Take a minute and read the steps below. Maybe you didn't even realize this was happening. Maybe one of the steps below is harder for you to keep from doing. Which step is the hardest to stop for you?

1. We ASSUME
2. We DWELL on it and get worked up.
3. We JUMP to conclusions
4. We ACCUSE

Maybe just recognizing you are doing it will help you stop before you get to the accusation of your husband. Take a minute and ask the Holy Spirit to help you believe the best, trust and be still, and wait until you hear both sides of the story.

Consider this wisdom from *Proverbs 18:17 NIV, "In a lawsuit the first to speak seems right, until someone comes forward and cross examines."* Until you hear both sides of the story, you do not have the whole picture and cannot judge. As you grow in exercising self-control in this way, you will find strength and a sense of dignity.

This word dignity isn't used that much today, but dignity is the state of being worthy of honor or respect. That may sound like something only available to an older woman, but Proverbs tells us that dignity is a mark of an excellent wife. *"Strength and dignity are her clothing, and she smiles at the future."* Prov 31:25 NASB We can choose to become women of dignity! We can carry ourselves as honorable women who choose self- control, and use our words to strengthen and encourage our husbands and those around us.

I've probably been married longer than you've been alive, and I am still working on controlling my tongue. I know that it will be a lifelong pursuit, but I am not going to give up. In loving our husbands, if we aspire to life-giving words and apologizing when we get it wrong, we will be considered a wise woman who builds up her home. I believe that you want that for yourself, too; so toward that end, I pray that you find yourself walking in self-control with your words and experience the strength of a woman who is clothed with dignity!

CHAPTER FOURTEEN

Children

I believe that God matches parents and children. I believe he is wise and purposeful about it. I also believe he selected me to be Mary, Anna, John, Warren, Patrick, and Amy's mother. God entrusted imperfect me with these beautiful new lives! What a humbling privilege it is to know that regardless of my weaknesses, he chose me to be their mom. Each one of them arrived hardwired and blessed with gifts and destinies that continue to unfold as they get older. There is so much about parenting that I don't understand. Questions like, "Why do some couples have such a tough time getting pregnant, while others who aren't even trying find themselves expecting? And why is adoption often such a challenging journey? And then there's the mystery of why some kids rebel even when their parents are incredible? I wish I had all the answers, but one thing I'm certain of is that God is always good.

God is sovereignly in charge, and I know that if the Bible has a promise about children, I can claim that promise for my child. And *you* can claim that promise for your child, too.

I know that in my weak places, where I feel inadequate or unsure, God's strength shines through. He doesn't just fill in the gaps; he transforms my weaknesses into opportunities for his power and grace to be revealed. This truth isn't just for me—it applies to you as well. We all have our struggles and doubts, but it's in those very moments that God shows up with his unwavering strength and love. So, let's begin here and fill in the blanks and declare this over our lives.

_____, God picked you for _____. On purpose. _____ needs YOU. God knows all of my strengths and weaknesses and He still picked ME to be _____'s mother. Perhaps my weaknesses are the very thing _____ needs to see to point him/her to God. Wherever I am lacking, God is going to fill in the gaps. He is not surprised by my weaknesses. He did not make a mistake when He blessed me with _____. I am the absolute best mom for what God is shaping within him/her, and the plans and purposes he has for their life."

I really believe that about me and my children. And I believe it about you and your children, too!

What truth do you need to believe about yourself as a parent today?

_____

_____

One thing that is not often discussed these days is the idea of seeking God's guidance in the decision to have children and determining the number of children to have. What did God say to Adam and Eve, the very first married couple?

"God blessed them and said to them, "Be _____ and

_____ . Fill the earth and govern it. Rule over the fish in the sea, the birds in the sky, and all the animals that scurry along the ground." Gen 1:28 NLT

God blessed the couple and then pronounced both a blessing and a command. Practically, what do you think this verse means? What if money wasn't an object, would it still mean the same thing to you?

_____

_____

In Psalm 127:3, God tells us how he views children. Read the verse and fill in the blanks below.

Children are _____

The fruit of the womb is _____

Different translations use different words to fill in these blanks, and I like each one. Write out the definition of each italicized word, and then reflect on how you would best phrase this scripture if you were clinging to its truth in your own circumstance.

Children are a *heritage*:

_____

_____

Children are a *gift:*

_____

_____

Children are an *inheritance*:

_____

_____

The fruit of the womb is a *reward*:

_____

_____

The fruit of the womb is a *gift*:

_____

_____

The fruit of the womb is a real *blessing*:

_____

_____

Now translate Psalm 127:3 in your own words:

_____

_____

Steve and I were engaged and discussing our future. I mentioned to him that I thought we should wait at least two years before trying to get pregnant, based on advice from a friend. She had suggested that waiting would allow us to get acclimated to married life and have time to enjoy each other, which sounded wise to me. However, two months into our engagement, I had a surprising experience. During one of my walks, I heard a quiet voice that I recognized as God's voice, saying that he wanted to plan the arrival of my babies. I felt stunned and thought to myself, "That will take some faith!" And after pondering it, I didn't share this experience with Steve. I reasoned that if God spoke to me, I wanted him to speak to Steve too. And he did. For Steve, it came in the form of a book we both read in preparation for marriage. The author referenced several scriptures that addressed children in the Bible. Foremost of all, "Children are a blessing," (Ps 127:3) and "God opens and closes the womb" (Gen 29:11 and 1 Sam 1-2). "We don't know the future of our fertility," the author asserted; therefore, the real wisdom is trusting God to give us children in his perfect timing." Steve asked me if I thought I could do that and I was overjoyed that God had spoken to Steve separately! Together, we decided that we would say yes to God's timing.

It takes faith to say yes and let God plan your family. It also takes faith to ask for God's wisdom as the two of you talk about what you'd like for your family. Whichever you choose, seek to honor God with your faith. I'd encourage you to pray that he directs you as you make decisions about your family. God knows the future. He knows what is coming. He knows what you have the capacity for, and he knows how you will grow and mature in the years to come.

What did the apostles pray in Luke 17:5?

_____

_____

Considering what the Bible says about children, how does your heart respond?

_____

_____

As you think about it, do you have any fears about becoming a parent and/or whether or not you'll be a successful parent?

_____

_____

Our culture has shifted from encouraging women to grow up and become mothers, to a focus on education and careers. Therefore it can be quite difficult for a career woman to justify taking a break to stay home and have children. Many women fear that they will lose themselves when they have children. Some women fear that they will be bored or lonely or not challenged if they stay home with their children.

Reread Christiana Kuhlow's quote from *Hey Beginner Wife*:

> *"Sometimes the reason women struggle with the transition to motherhood is because they're comparing their new life as a mother to their childless years. There seems to be this*

*notion that who a woman was when she was single is who
she is, that children throw a wrench in the works, and that
she has to "get back to" whoever she was before that. But
why? Singleness isn't equilibrium, and having a family isn't
disequilibrium. It's one thing to be unfamiliar with
mothering, and the new season it brings. Speaking of this as
a tragic loss that must be grieved is quite another. Of course,
we change in motherhood. Change also accompanies career
shifts. So why do we celebrate the "evolving" and
"shedding" accompanying every other season of life except
motherhood?"*

Do you identify with the feeling that mothering will bring the
loss of your identity?

_____

_____

Once you become a parent, what do you anticipate missing from
your childless years?

_____

_____

***

If you're reading this and thinking, "Well, I sure don't like the
parents he picked for me," I am so sorry. For a variety of reasons,
there are definitely men and women who have done a miserable job
of parenting and their children are paying the price. What consoles

me about this is the fact that WE have the opportunity to change our family history and create our own story. We can learn to be the parent we never had. (We didn't get to pick our parents, but we DO get to choose our spouse and create a new family.)

In God's infinite wisdom, he uses marriage to establish families and provide a safe place for children to thrive. He also uses children to connect us to the future and further establish our purposes on earth. (Don't misunderstand this to mean that couples with children have no purpose, I am not saying that. God is intimately involved in each marriage and marks each marriage with a calling which may or may not include children. Either way, we can trust that he is a good God. He is infinitely kind, perfectly wise, and wants the absolute best for us.) And just as marriage refines us, having children requires us to grow up and mature and make our lives about something other than ourselves. Just as the process of marriage ultimately makes us more like Jesus, parenting does too.

CHAPTER FIFTEEN

Aligned Values

Have you ever felt so frustrated with your husband that it seems like you're a volcano about to erupt? You've kept your complaints bottled up for so long that it feels inevitable that you're going to blow. Every internal complaint against your husband seems to strengthen your argument, and you can list example after example to prove your point—that you're right and he's wrong.

I found myself in this position when I was pregnant with our fifth child and Steve was working 15 hour days. I was so upset with him that I didn't trust myself to even make my case before him. I knew I would say something hurtful, and as much as I wanted things to change my goal was not to hurt him.

So, on a Sunday afternoon while he lay on the couch and the kids were taking their naps, I went to the backyard and turned my complaints into a long-winded prayer to the Lord. I outlined everything I was upset about.

(*Excerpt from* **Hey Beginner Wife**)

> *With each lap, I listed the areas of Steve's selfishness. As I ranted, I reminded Jesus of what I had to do every day. I reminded him that Steve got to work in an air conditioned office, while I had to wear compression socks just to manage my pregnancy-induced circulation issues, in a house that*

163

was regularly 90 degrees in the summer heat. I reminded him that I hadn't paid to have my hair cut in over a year, and cheerfully cut my own children's hair. I complained that my girlfriend's husband would come home and give her children a bath, read them a story, and HE would tuck them into bed. If she needed help with the housework, he routinely vacuumed and cleaned the kitchen for her. Then, I started listing what I perceived to be Steve's lack of spiritual leadership. My husband never suggested that we pray together, nor did he lead any sort of family devotion. Miniature lap after miniature lap, I vomited my complaints before God. As I write this now, I am embarrassed to admit the depth of my accusations against my husband and how wronged I felt by him. I poured out my complaints until I had exhausted my list, and then I walked a few laps in silence.

As I continued my silent laps, I heard a quiet response. A still, small voice within me said, "You are too hard on him."

I stopped walking, simultaneously stunned and humbled. In that moment I saw Steve from a different perspective and I realized it was the truth: I really was too hard on him.

It was as if God came and gently took my arm, and said, "Come look at it from where I sit." All of a sudden, I saw the weight Steve was carrying. My 32-year-old husband had the responsibility to provide for a pregnant wife and four children. A responsibility we both agreed we wanted, and he was stewarding as best he could. What a massive weight for a 32-year-old to bear. Most other men his age either weren't married, had only one child, or had a wife who was also bringing home a paycheck. Because of Steve's great conviction to give me the opportunity to stay home and raise our children, he worked 15 hours a day to make it happen. It wasn't like he was out in the evenings with friends, he was working to provide for his family.

At the age of 32, he was a business owner and carefully making sure that he paid his contracted employee before he paid himself. Steve prioritized coming home every night to have dinner with our family before heading back to the office. And though we didn't have much time together, he made sure that we had quality time around the table every night. Was I really so selfish that I would begrudge him an afternoon on the couch?

Looking back, I'm thankful that I went to the Lord and cried out to him and that the Holy Spirit met me in my weakness with his love and direction.

What two things happen when we cry out to the Lord?

Psalm 34:17 NKJV

"The righteous cry out, and the LORD hears, and delivers them out of all their troubles."

_____

_____

2 Sam 22:3-4 NKJV

"The God of my strength, in whom I will trust; my shield and the horn of my salvation, my stronghold and my refuge; my Savior, You save me from violence. I will call upon the LORD, who is worthy to be praised; so shall I be saved from my enemies."

After Samuel called upon the Lord, what expectation did he have?

_____

_____

In Psalm 116:1-4 TPT, the author speaks of an intimate relationship with God. As you read his words it's easy to picture him overcome with joy as he exclaims, *"I am passionately in love with God because he listens to me. He hears my prayers and answers them. As long as I live I'll keep praying to him, for he stoops down to listen to my heart's cry...I cried out to the Lord, "God, come and save me!" He was so kind, so gracious to me."*

Close your eyes and imagine approaching God with your heart's cry. Can you picture a God who stoops down to listen? Can you imagine that his response to you is kind and gracious? How would you respond in return?

_____

_____

Maybe you had a hard time picturing God's gentle and gracious response to you. I encourage you to take a few minutes and ask the Holy Spirit to help you believe that God is so FOR you!

Isn't it amazing that God invites us to cry out to him? When was the last time that you cried out to God?

_____

_____

As our father, God welcomes our cries. Do you really believe that? How would believing that change your prayer life?

_____

_____

On that Sunday afternoon, while I prayed, venting my frustrations about my husband, I finally finished and fell silent. I expected God to respond and defend me. Eager to hear his answer, I listened. I thought he would quietly acknowledge the everyday care I provided for my children. Or maybe he would commend my resourcefulness and express pride in the extra effort I put into my grocery list to stay within budget. Have you approached God in prayer with an expectation that he will answer you in a specific way? Or have you prayed and told him exactly how you'd like him to answer you?

_____

_____

Can you give an example of a time when God has answered one of your prayers? How did you know that it was a specific answer to your prayer?

_____

_____

John 10:27-28 KJV

My sheep _____ _____ _____*, and I know them, and they follow me.*

In 1 Kings 19:11-12 Elijah encounters God. We read that God's voice was not found in a fierce hurricane-like wind, an earthquake, or a fire. Where was God's voice found?

_____

_____

After my monologue, I hoped to hear God's still, small voice like Elijah did. Have you ever heard him speak to you in a still voice, through a friend, or through a Bible verse?

_____

_____

As believers in Christ, God offers us his nearness in prayer. He promises that he hears our cries and that He will defend us. I assumed that God would defend *me* after I complained about Steve, but when he answered me it was actually Steve that he defended. In the quietness of my thoughts, I heard God say, "You're too hard on him." Instantly, I saw Steve from God's perspective. Where other men his age weren't yet married, or were married with one or two children, Steve was responsible for so much more and he wasn't complaining about it.

With this new perspective also came an understanding that I needed to apologize to God for the anger and bitterness I felt toward Steve. In that moment I knew that God had met me right in the midst of my bitterness and he was holding me accountable for my attitude because he wanted me to be free of the heavy weight of my bitterness. Once I prayed a prayer of repentance to God, my heart felt light and I felt tender toward Steve and all he was doing for our family.

Ephesians 4:31-32 ESV

Let all bitterness and wrath and anger and clamor and slander

be _____   _____

_____ _____, *along with all*

malice. Be kind to one another, tenderhearted, _____

_____ _____, *as God in Christ forgave you.*
Ephesians 4:31-32 ESV

What about you? Are you fighting bitterness towards your spouse in your own heart? Bitterness is like drinking poison and waiting for the other person to die. It hurts you, and it hurts the marriage relationship. Read the verse below (you filled in the blanks above) and check your heart.

Let all bitterness and wrath and anger and clamor and slander be put away from you, along with all malice. Be kind to one another, tenderhearted, forgiving one another, as God in Christ forgave you. Eph 4:31-32 ESV

Here are just a few symptoms that might suggest bitterness. Check any that may apply:

- The grudges are silently building in your heart.
- You constantly feel angry.
- You avoid conversations you know you need to have.
- You use the phrases "You always… or, you never…"
- You are quick to snap and explode when the offense doesn't warrant such a dramatic reaction.
- You're finding it increasingly difficult to trust your husband.

God invites us into a relationship with him, and prayer can be as simple as an honest conversation with him. Isn't it amazing that the God who created us and sits in the heavens welcomes our prayers? We can complain and argue and ask him questions, and he welcomes it all. Conversational prayer has several benefits. It helps us feel closer to God and relieves our stress by allowing us to hand over our problems and concerns to him and ask for his help in caring for them. When I pray, I like to imagine handing God a huge armful of my worries.

Prayer isn't just about what we gain but also about how it changes us and blesses those we pray for, especially our husbands. After I finally opened up to God about all my frustrations with what my husband wasn't doing right, something inside me shifted. Instead of dwelling on my disappointments, my heart softened towards him.

Suddenly, I found myself earnestly asking God to bless Steve with his very best.

During that season, I discovered Stormie Omartian's book, "The Power of a Praying Wife," and it resonated with me. I started praying a different prayer for my husband every day using her book, which is divided into 31 chapters, each focusing on a specific need husbands have. Stormie backs each prayer with Scripture, showing us that God wants to answer these prayers for us. She also teaches wives how to pray for themselves in a humble way alongside their prayers for their husbands. Here's an example of a prayer from her chapter, *His Wife.*

"Give me a new, positive, joyful, loving, forgiving attitude toward him. Where he has erred, reveal it to him and convict his heart about it. Lead him through the paths of repentance and deliverance. Help me not to hold myself apart from him emotionally, mentally, or physically because of unforgiveness. Where either of us needs to ask for forgiveness from the other, help us to do so. If there is something I'm not seeing that is adding to this problem, reveal it to me and help me to understand it."[5] Can you imagine God's response upon hearing this prayer? We are asking him to do all of the things he longs to do! Of course he will want to answer our prayers! What I especially value about Stormie's example is the continual reminder that though our husband may need prayer, we are not perfect either.

---

5   Stormie Omartian, *The Power of a Praying Wife,* (Harvest House: Eugene, 2014) 28.

What thoughts do you have about conversational prayer with God? Are you already doing this? Would you be comfortable praying like this?

_____

_____

Journaling can be another form of conversational prayer. Many women use their journals to share their hearts with God and to ask for his intervention. Instead of taking their complaints to a girlfriend to unburden their hearts, they pick up their journals and process their thoughts on paper. I've also found it helpful to write. However, if I know that I don't ever want someone to read what I'm writing (I want it to remain between me and God for all of time) I will write on a single piece of paper. Once I have unburdened my heart and released my worries to God, I usually feel peace restored to my heart and I shred the paper, or otherwise destroy it.

Matthew 11:28-29 ESV

Come to me, all who labor and are heavy laden, and I will give you rest. Take my yoke upon you, and learn from me, for I am gentle and lowly in heart, and you will find rest for your souls.

Do you know what it means to carry a burden in your heart about your husband or your marriage? What does Matthew 11:28-29 tell us about taking our burdens to the Lord?

_____

_____

Proverbs 14:1-25 NLT. *A wise woman builds her home, but a foolish woman tears it down with her own hands.*

Proverbs 14 tells us that a wise woman *builds* her home. For me, this means guarding the words of my mouth and speaking words of truth and encouragement both in my inner dialogue and to my family. I consider whether the books on my shelves, the music I listen to, and what I watch on television are contributing to the woman I desire to be. As a mother, I'm mindful that I'm investing in the wellbeing of my family when I set a good example. I also employ conversational prayer as a practical investment that builds up my home, my marriage and my family.

It's chapter fifteen, and you and I have been together long enough for me to let you in on a secret: Turning to Jesus in prayer is the ultimate secret to my happy marriage and the power in my parenting. I cannot think of anything in my marriage that I haven't talked to the Lord about. When we first married, I focused on Steve becoming the best version of himself and I corrected him accordingly. I prayed with the same intention, focusing on how I wanted God to change him. And then I learned firsthand that God usually answers prayers like mine to change the wife and her heart first. God revealed bitterness in my heart toward my husband; and *my* selfishness and *my* unforgiveness. Because God saw how my sin contributed to the tension in our marriage, he played the long game and worked to change my heart first. He opened my eyes to what I needed to work on, and in prayer I asked God for forgiveness. Then, in the situations where it was appropriate, I went and asked my husband for forgiveness.

Through prayer I've learned that I don't have authority over my husband, but I do have spiritual authority to address the unseen attacks on my husband and our marriage in the spiritual realm. This has transformed my prayers from focusing on my husband as the problem to seeing God as the answer to the struggle. It has encouraged me to view my prayers as effective weapons in a spiritual battle with the power to bring victory for us and our marriage.

"We don't have authority over our husbands. However, we have been given authority "over all the power of the enemy" (Luke 10:19) and can do great damage to the enemy's plans when we pray. Many difficult things that happen in a marriage relationship are actually part of the enemy's plan for its demise. But we can say this:

> "I will not allow anything to destroy my marriage."
>
> "I will not stand by and watch my husband be wearied, beaten down, or destroyed."
>
> "I will not sit idle while an invisible wall goes up between us."
>
> "I will not allow confusion, miscommunication, wrong attitudes, and bad choices to erode what we are trying to build together."
>
> "I will not tolerate hurt and unforgiveness leading us to divorce."

We can take a stand against any negative influences in our marriage relationship and know that God has given us authority in his name to back it up.

You have the means to establish a hedge of protection around your marriage because Jesus said, "Whatever you bind on earth will be bound in heaven, and whatever you loose on earth will be loosed in heaven." (Matthew 18:18) You have authority in the name of Jesus to stop evil and proclaim good for your family. You can submit to God in prayer whatever controls your husband– alcoholism, workaholism, laziness, depression, infirmity, abusiveness, anxiety, fear, or failure– and pray for him to be released from it."[6]

As a newlywed, I wasn't encouraged to invite Jesus into my marriage through prayer, so it is important to me to make sure that I reach you with this message at the beginning of your marriage. No matter where you are my friend, start now. I think you'll discover, as I have, that in prayer you can fight for your loved ones and take authority over lies and accusations that attack your family. You'll also find that prayer is a go-to comfort when you long to feel known and accepted. Conversational prayer connects us to God in a way few things can. Prayer is powerful. It will change you. It will change your marriage. It will give you the strength and wisdom you need to become an absolutely amazing wife.

---

6   Ibid, 14-15.

Chapter Sixteen

It's Worth It!

Conversation: Heart to Heart

"It would seem that Our Lord finds our desires not too strong, but too weak. We are half-hearted creatures, fooling about with drink and sex and ambition when infinite joy is offered us, like an ignorant child who wants to go on making mud pies in a slum because he cannot imagine what is meant by the offer of a holiday at the sea. We are far too easily pleased."[7]

Is it possible that our desires for a sanctified marriage are too weak, as C.S. Lewis intimates in the quote above? Are we fooling around with a half-hearted commitment to our marriage by allowing little things to come between us, resentments to build, or selfishness to take root? Perhaps we are far too easily pleased, like the ignorant child happy to make mud pies because he simply doesn't know that something better is available to him? So we persist in a relationship that in comparison to our neighbor's marriage is slightly better, and never discover that God has something *much* better for us.

Covenant marriage is God's gift to us. I view covenant marriage as the "holiday at the sea" that Lewis mentions, while contract marriage is choosing something familiar like contenting ourselves with what's in our backyard. The offer of a holiday at sea doesn't

---

7   C.S. Lewis, *The Weight of Glory,* (Harper One, New York, 2001) 26.

tempt someone who cannot envision the sea; she doesn't know the beauty of the sea or the inner peace she'd experience as she listened to the waves lapping the shore, or the comfort of cool breezes on her skin. One cannot fault her because she is ignorant.

Some of us lack understanding about marriage because we've never witnessed a couple consistently believing the best in each other and overcoming challenges together. Others carry deep wounds from childhood—abandonment or abuse—that drain our energy for building a healthy marriage. Others of us lack a supportive community to cheer us on and lift us up in tough times. Yet, our God is big enough to help and provide a path for each of us to find the support and healing we need. This companion guide draws from Scripture to establish a foundation of God's truth, his presence, and his promises for us. It encourages us to pray, knowing that God hears and answers our prayers.

As we wrap up our study, and consider the foundation we've built our marriages upon, know that ***God is for you***. He designed marriage to make us more like him. He knew that everyone who marries will be challenged to choose selfLESSness over selfISHness. Every married person faces a daily choice: Will I strive to treat my spouse as Jesus treated others, or will I give in to weariness and prioritize my own needs today? Is maintaining my cheerfulness today truly significant?

Inspiration: God's Truth

The grass is not greener somewhere else. A different husband would not change anything. God's end goal is to make you more like

Jesus, and he does it when he reveals the attitudes in our heart. He exposes our attitudes, allowing us to understand what we're dealing with. This gives us the chance to apologize, seek change, and choose a better path. You may have noticed that certain aspects of ourselves only become evident in marriage. Like a refining fire, marriage brings out the impurities in our hearts, leaving us more beautiful if we allow the refiner to help us remove them.

God refines our hearts to make us more like him. We, as husband and wife, should respond by loving and affirming our commitment to our marriage. God's definition of love as recorded in 1 Corinthians, shows that he understands how the human heart naturally responds, without the power of being born again with a new heart. As you read this list, underline the natural human tendencies highlighted in his definition of love.

Love is large and incredibly patient.

Love is gentle and consistently kind to all.

It refuses to be jealous when blessing comes to someone else.

Love does not brag about one's achievements nor inflate its own importance.

Love does not traffic in shame and disrespect,

Nor selfishly seek its own honor.

Love is not easily irritated or quick to take offense.

Love joyfully celebrates honesty and finds no delight in what is wrong.

Love is a safe place of shelter, for it never stops believing the best for others.

Love never takes failure as defeat, for it never gives up.

Love never stops loving. (I Cor 13: 4-8a TPT)

Our natural tendencies to feel jealousy, show disrespect, take offense, or give up are overridden when we choose love. Isn't this the kind of love we all long for? When you promise to love and cherish through good and bad times, God makes this love available to you if you follow Christ.

I will "refine them as silver is refined, and test them as gold is tested. They will call on my name, and I will answer them; I will say, 'They are my people,' and they will say, 'The Lord is my God.' Zech 13:9 NASB Have you noticed how God has been refining your heart since you got married? When you feel this happening, do you find yourself calling on his name and listening for his response? Share your reflections below.

_____

_____

_____

In the Song of Solomon, the bridegroom lovingly affirms his bride-to-be, declaring her beauty to him: *"Let me see your radiant face and hear your sweet voice. How beautiful your eyes of worship and lovely your voice in prayer." (*Song of Solomon 2:14b TPT) However, after acknowledging both her natural and inner beauty, he speaks about their shared responsibility in their relationship. He encourages her to actively protect their love, saying, *"You must catch the troubling foxes, those sly little foxes that hinder our relationship for they raid our budding vineyard of love to ruin what I've planted within you. Will you catch them and remove them for me? We will do it together."* (Song of Solomon 2:14b-15 TPT)

The troubling foxes represent sin that sneaks in and has the power to ruin 'the vineyard of love' and what God has 'planted within' us. Take a minute to pray and ask God to identify a few "foxes" that you've allowed in your marriage that he would like you to remove. Write them below.

_____

_____

The bridegroom (Jesus) says to his bride-to-be (you), *"Will you catch them and remove them for me?"* And before she can even respond that she cannot do it herself, what does he promise?

"We will _____ _____ _____*."*

These five words fill my heart with joy! "We will do it together!" What a beautiful, generous, compassionate God we serve! God doesn't leave us to flounder through our difficult places alone. He doesn't shame us for our mistakes. As Christians, we have the privilege of inviting Jesus to walk alongside us. Yes, we will discover that marriage brings challenges we've never experienced, but amid our vulnerability with our spouse, when the hidden places of our hearts are revealed, we can lean on God's promise that he will walk us through it. He will never leave us or forsake us.

Moses spoke to those going into the promised land, *"Be strong and courageous. Do not fear or be in dread of them, for it is the Lord your God who goes with you. He will not leave you or forsake you."* *Deut 31:6 ESV*

Other translations phrase the last sentence with slight variations. Circle the words of the verse in different translations that most resonate with your heart that God will never leave you.

*"He will neither **fail** you nor **abandon** you."* NLT

*"He won't **let you down**; he won't **leave** you."* MSG

*"He will not **fail** you or **forsake** you."* NASB

What a comfort to know that we are not alone! In the context of marriage, God has done a refining work in my heart. My girlfriends have experienced it as well. We've experienced the promises of God coming to pass, and we've gone after the *'foxes that raid our vineyards'* seeking to ruin what God has planted in our marriage. We've known what it is to lay down our lives for our husbands and family.

Let me take a minute to highlight what Jesus told his disciples about following him and what it would look like. It's not often talked about, and it's important in our understanding of our relationship with Christ.

"Then Jesus said to his disciples, "If you truly want to follow me, you should at once completely reject and disown your own life. And you must be willing to share my cross and experience it as your

own, as you continually surrender to my ways. For if you choose self-sacrifice and lose your lives for my glory, you will continually discover true life. But if you choose to keep your lives for yourselves, you will forfeit what you try to keep." Matt 16:24-25 TPT

We are promised that we will discover true life if we "*choose*

_____-_____, *and* _____ (*y*)*our*

_____" for his glory.

Consider this translation, and the slightly different word choices:

"Then Jesus told his disciples, "If anyone would come after me, let him deny himself and take up his cross and follow me. For whoever would save his life would lose it, but whoever loses his life for my sake will find it." Matt 16:24-25 ESV

Which phrases stand out to you as worded differently? Underline them and then write down what you think it means to '*choose self-sacrifice and lose your life/seek to save your life.*'

_____

_____

_____

This can be a tough message. Have you heard it before? How does it make you feel?

_____

_____

Self-sacrifice does not mean harming your body or depriving yourself of necessary nutrition for health. Rather, it involves choosing not to seek personal comfort at times when someone else has a pressing need that aligns with what Jesus would want you to do. This might mean forgoing a relaxing evening in front of the television because your baby has a fever and only settles when you walk them around the house. It could be responding to a neighbor's urgent request to watch their children while they rush another child to the ER. Or, it could mean accompanying your husband for a walk in the park after a tough day at work when you'd rather just sit on the couch. Most of us don't wake up hoping that we will be asked to make a sacrifice today. By its very definition, sacrifice indicates a suffered loss. But Jesus teaches that if we choose self-sacrifice and lose our lives for his sake, we will continually discover true life. It takes faith to believe that. And it takes faith to approach marriage with this mindset! Most marriages fail today because one or both of the partners come to the marriage looking for what they can get from the other. Even a casual observer of history can see that broken homes and unhappy marriages are more prevalent now than ever before. Jesus provided the key to a thriving marriage when he taught, *"It is more blessed to give than to receive." Acts 20:35 NIV*

We must approach our marriage with a mindset to *give* to our partner. Sacrificing for one another becomes a mutual expression of love in the Christian marriage. It can even become a habit that no longer feels like a painful sacrifice. You come to know that as you accommodate your husband's needs he will accommodate yours, and vice versa. And, my dear friend, if your husband is not there yet it does not mean that he never will be! If, in your love for him, he tends to take and rarely give back to you, I would encourage you to consider your acts of love for him as obedience to the Lord Jesus. Do it for his sake. Ask God to honor you for your obedience. Consider what Jesus said and make your sacrifices for *his glory.* (*"For if you choose self-sacrifice and* **lose your lives for my glory....**" *Matt 16:24-25 TPT)* Pray and ask God to be glorified when you deny yourself and love your husband when he is unlovable.[8]

When we love our husbands as Christ loved us, we are fulfilling what Jesus called the greatest commandment, *"You shall love the Lord your God with all your heart and with all your soul and with all your mind...You shall love your neighbor as yourself."* Matt *22:37-39 ESV*

Our love stands out in a world where self-interest often takes priority. And our marriages become truly unique when we prioritize our spouse's needs over our own.

"You are the light of the world—like a city on a hilltop that cannot be hidden. No one lights a lamp and then puts it under a basket. Instead, a lamp is placed on a stand, where it gives light to everyone in the house. In the same way, let **your good deeds** *shine out for all to see, so that everyone will praise your heavenly Father."* Matt 5:14-16 NLT

*"**As a result of your ministry**, they will give glory to God. For your generosity to them and to all believers will prove that you are obedient to the good news of Christ."* 2 Cor 9:13 NLT

---

8   If you are being physically abused and are not safe in your home, please seek the help offered in your community. In the United States, the Domestic Violence hotline is 800-799-7233. (Interpretation is available for 200+ languages.) Or text BEGIN to 88788 for help.

What happens when others see 'your good deeds'?

_____

_____

What happens 'as a result of your ministry'?

_____

_____

God calls us to imitate him. Who are we trying to please? In the verses below, underline the phrase that shows the author's motivation. Is our ultimate goal to please God? Or are we striving to please others? Learning to live for an audience of one (God) will help keep us from letting other people steal our peace.

"Obviously, I'm not trying to win the approval of people, but of God. If pleasing people were my goal, I would not be Christ's servant." Gal 1:10 NLT

"Imitate God, therefore, in everything you do, because you are his dear children. Live a life filled with love, following the example of Christ. He loved us and offered himself as a sacrifice for us, a pleasing aroma to God." Eph 5:1-2

"Work willingly at whatever you do, as though you were working for the Lord rather than for people. Remember that the Lord will give you an inheritance as your reward, and that the master you are serving is Christ." Col 3:23-24 NLT

"And whatever you do, whether in word or deed, do it all in the name of the Lord Jesus, giving thanks to God the Father through him." Col 3:17 NIV

In ***Hey Beginner Wife***, I quoted the theologian Dietrich Bonhoeffer and the words he wrote to his niece encouraging her about the powerful office of marriage. Now, at the end of our study, let's read the quote again.

"Marriage is more than your love for each other. It has a higher dignity and power, for it is God's holy ordinance, through which he wills to perpetuate the human race til the end of time. In your love you see only your two selves in the world, but in your marriage you are a link in the chain of the generations. In your love you see only the heaven of your own happiness, but in marriage you are placed at a post of responsibility towards the world and mankind. Your love is your own private possession, but marriage is more than something personal - it is a status, an office. Just as it is the crown, and not merely the will to rule, that makes the king, so it is marriage, and not merely your love for each other, that joins you together in the sign of God and man. From now on, it is not your love that sustains the marriage, but the marriage that sustains your love."[9]

We know what Bonhoeffer speaks of. We've all seen couples consumed with "the heaven of their own happiness." Couples so in love that they see only themselves. Here, Bonhoeffer speaks to these couples and encourages them to consider that their love for one another is not given just for their own personal pleasure. God has a higher plan for the gift of love. God gave us marriage, and Bonhoeffer teaches that marriage is more than something personal, it's a 'status and an office.' He writes that there is a responsibility inherent in marriage to be a 'link in the chain of generations.' A husband and wife take the traditions, wisdom, and understanding of the

---

9   Dietrich Bonhoeffer, *Letters & Papers From Prison* (Touchstone: New York, 1977) 42-43.

generations before them and pass them on to their children just as
God commanded the people of Israel: *"...commit yourselves
wholeheartedly to these commands that I am giving you today.
Repeat them again and again to your children. Talk about them
when you are at home and when you are on the road, when you are
going to bed and when you are getting up." Deut 6:6-7 NLT*

Marriage and family is the structure God provided for children
to feel safe and provided for and to learn the ways of God. Each
family creates a building block in the structure of society, so the
health of the family is integral to the health of a nation. This makes
marriage something much larger than just the two of you. Therefore,
the work you invest in your marriage strengthens the foundation of
the family *and* the culture around you.

Bonhoeffer highlights that while our love for one another is a
beautiful gift that belongs privately to the two of us, this love will be
best sustained within the gift of marriage. When the fond feelings of
fresh love fade, it is the commitment of marriage that requires us to
stay and work through the challenges. Marriage gives us a safe arena
to figure things out, learn how to selfLESSly love each other, and
get to the finish line even more thankful for one another.

Bonhoeffer packed quite a lot into two paragraphs. Underline
what he says marriage is, and then answer this question in the lines
below: How does your marriage sustain and protect your love?

_____

_____

_____

God speaks directly to us about divorce with some straight-forward language: *"Didn't the Lord make you one with your wife? In body and spirit you are his…so guard your heart; remain loyal to the wife of your youth. "For I hate divorce!" says the Lord, the God of Israel. "To divorce your wife is to overwhelm her with cruelty," says the Lord of Heaven's Armies. So guard your heart; do not be unfaithful to your wife." Mal 2:15-16 NLT*

In this verse God reminds us that we become one when we get married. He reminds us that we belong to him— in body and in spirit. The ESV translates verse 15 this way: *"Did he not make them one, with a portion of the Spirit in their union?" Mal 2:15.* When we marry, God enters our marriage with a portion of the Holy Spirit dwelling in our union. He intricately weaves us together as husband and wife, creating a new work of art with just the two of us. One preacher aptly put it, 'Divorce desecrates a creative masterpiece.' Just as Leonardo da Vinci would have felt devastated if the Mona Lisa were torn in two, God feels severe grief when a marriage ends because it is the ripping apart of two people he entwined together in a work of outstanding artistry. Understanding this should encourage all of us to persevere through the challenges of marriage, knowing that God celebrates, values, and is forever committed to the unions he has created.

Conversation: Heart to Heart

In many ways marriage is a journey of perseverance and endurance. Do you remember the story I shared as an analogy to highlight this very thing in *Hey Beginner Wife*? I spoke of Steve's drum corps experience and how the corps invested their whole summer to perfecting one final performance. Here's an excerpt:

Steve tells me that their lives were not their own. The corps leaders decided their schedule for the entire day from the moment they woke up. They were told when they would practice, when they would eat, and when they would sleep. It was grueling, but at the end of the season, their final show was stunning. The competition was so severe that it wasn't unusual for the top three corps to finish within tenths of a percentage point against each other.

Steve shared with me that it was exhausting and exhilarating, but he would repeat it in a heartbeat. The friendships he forged were lifelong. The experience of putting his all into the goal of one final spectacular performance was so rewarding that it was addictive. His whole summer had a purpose greater than himself. Every mundane day, every tiny detail of hitting the exact note and marching in unison mattered because it culminated in something that could never be achieved without sacrifice and grit. Not a year goes by that he doesn't think about those summers.

Few things in life require us to give our all, sacrifice, and work to the point of exhaustion for the greater good. What's your end goal?

Application: Putting Love Into Action

Steve's drum corps' goal was to win the national championship. Reflect for a moment on yourself, your husband, and your marriage. Do you both have a shared goal for your marriage? Take a moment to write down your shared goal below. If you haven't established one yet, consider jotting down a few things that could potentially become your goal if you agreed together.

_____

_____

_____

If you have trouble thinking of goals for your marriage, maybe use one of these? Check any that could start the conversation with your husband of setting goals for your marriage:

- To train your children to have great love and affection for each other.

_____

- To be generous givers, no matter what your income.

_____

- Volunteer together. Choose an organization and sign up!

_____

- Be debt free; budget together and celebrate every victory along the way.

_____

- To go on a mission trip-domestic or international— once every XX years.

_____

- Less screen time. (Maybe designate screen-free time. Play cards, take a walk, etc. Just enjoy undistracted time together!)

  _____

- Commit to more date nights. Get creative!

  _____

- Create a new relational ritual habit (For example, have coffee together every morning.)

  _____

- Tell each other 3 things you are grateful for every day.

  _____

- Set 20 minutes aside each day to cuddle together.

  _____

- Take a romantic getaway. (This could be for hours, a weekend, or a longer trip. Even a staycation could be fun!)

  _____

- Celebrate your life together more! (Yes, even the little things! Open a bottle of champagne, use your fine china, dress up for a date!)

  _____

As you stand at the threshold of the rest of your life, I'd like to leave you with this verse that sums up my prayer for you. When you think about your marriage—what it is now and what you dream it to be—I pray you grasp what truly matters. May you grow stronger and better together, and may those moments in your life where you say yes to Jesus and no to selfISHness weave a beautiful tapestry in your marriage—a masterpiece of two lives joined and knit together for God's glory!

"I pray that your love will overflow more and more, and that you will keep on growing in knowledge and understanding. For I want you to understand what really matters, so that you may live pure and blameless lives until the day of Christ's return. May you always be filled with the fruit of your salvation—the righteous character produced in your life by Jesus Christ—for this will bring much glory and praise to God." Phil 1:9-11 NLT

I'm so proud of you my friend. Marriage is a beautiful and rewarding journey! I pray your journey together is filled with joy, blessings and endless opportunities to grow closer to each other and to our exceptional God.

I'm in your corner,

Xoxo

About the Author

Michelle Lentz graduated from UCLA with a degree in English Literature. Using her happy marriage of nearly 40 years as an example, she writes to inspire women to learn from her mistakes, love their husbands well and enjoy marriage. When shes not cheering on her husband Steve and their six grown children and five delightful grandchildren, she's curled up with a good book, pursuing a deep conversation, or looking forward to the next wedding so she can hit the dance floor. You can find her on Instagram at @heybeginnerwife.

Made in United States
Troutdale, OR
12/02/2024

25735399R10125